AN INTRODUCTION TO
COELENTERATA

AJAY PUBLISHERS & DISTISTRIBUTORS
Behind Motimaszid, Near Sulemania School
BHOPAL-462 001

AN
INTRODUCTION TO
COELENTERATA

By

H.S. Bhamrah
Kavita Juneja

Edited by

Balvinder K.

ANMOL PUBLICATIONS PVT. LTD.
NEW DELHI - 110 002 (INDIA)

ANMOL PUBLICATIONS PVT. LTD.

4374/4B, Ansari Road, Daryaganj
New Delhi - 110 002

An Introduction to Coelenterata

© Authors

First Edition, 1991

Reprint, 1992, 1999

Second Revised Edition, 2001

ISBN 81-261-0683-2

PRINTED IN INDIA

Published by J.L. Kumar for Anmol Publications Pvt. Ltd., New Delhi - 110 002 and Printed at Mehra Offset Press, Delhi.

Contents

PREFACE

An Introduction to Coelenterata is the revised and enlarged second edition of the book. It has been designed to approach the morphology, anatomy, physiology and development of selected type in a simple and lucid style. The approach to the discussion of all the types is very simple so as to impact to the students a clear and vivid understanding. According to the scheme of treatment the important animal types of the phylum have been dealt with first, and efforts have been made to present their elaborate and uptodate account. General characters and classification and brief description of other important types of the phylum have also been dealt with complete, authentic and uptodate account. Further separate chapters on topics of significance and general interest pertaining to the phylum have also been added to make the treatment more elaborate.

It has been the constant endeavour of the authors to furnish maximum substance, keeping in view the limitations of size of the volume. Efforts have been made to condense the matter as far as practicable. The book features both a text and a laboratory guide. It is hoped that this book will not only meet the requirement of Indian students but will also be useful as a guideline to the teachers in their teaching.

There can be no claim to originality except in the manner of treatment and much of the information has been obtained from the books and scientific journals available in different libraries.

The authors express their thanks to their friends and colleagues whose constant inspiration have initiated them to bring out this book.

In this edition all the errors of first edition have been rectified. New information is incorporated in the light of recent developments and latest research. Teachers and scholars can send their criticism and suggestions to further improve the contents.

Authors

Coelenterata : Characters & Classification

Coelenterata was formerly regarded as Phylum divided into two subphyla : Subphylum Cnidaria including *Hydra, Obelia, Aurelia,* Corals and Sea-anemones, and Subphylum Acnidaria including Ctenophora (*Pleurobrachia, Beroe* etc.). But during recent years *Hyman* (1940), *Barnes* (1980) and others regard the Coelenterata (Cnidaria) and Acnidaria as two distinct phyla on the basis of a number of dissimilarities between the two.

The coelenterates are regarded as primitive Metazoa in which the cells are organized to reach the tissue stage. In fact, all the basic types of tissues of higher animals are found in them viz. epithelial tissue for covering the body, muscular tissue for support, nervous tissue for conduction of stimuli and reproductive tissue for the reproduction.

Derivation of Name

All the coelenterates possess a single large cavity, the *gastrovascular cavity*. This cavity performs the function of digestion and distribution of digested food materials. It has one exit, the mouth. Term Coelenterata was first used by *Leuckart* (1847) for those animals in which the enteric cavity form the body cavity. The name Coelenterata has been derived from two Greek words, *Koilos* = hollow, *enteron* = intestine. Thus the name of this phylum literally means hollow intestine but hollow bodies is considered more appropriate because actual intestine is not found in coelenterates.

General Characters

1. They are simplest Metazoa showing the cell-tissue grade of organization.
2. All the members of this phylum are aquatic, most of whom are marine others are found in fresh water, none is parasitic.
3. They are either colonial or solitary. They are sedentary or free-swimming.

4. Symmetry is usually *radial* about an oral-aboral axis. In some forms, however, it is *biradial.*

5. Head and segmentation is absent.

6. They exhibit two different body forms, the *medusa* which is adopted for a pelagic existence and the *polyp*, which is adapted for an attachment benthic existence. Colonial forms have evolved in many polypoid forms.

7. One or more whorls of tentacles encircling the mouth at one end of the body. These are used for food-capturing, ingestion and defence.

8. The soft and delicate body may be supported by horny or calcareous exoskeleton or endoskeleton.

9. The body-wall is composed of two layers of cells (*diploblastic*), the outer epidermis and inner endodermis or gastrodermis, and an intervening *mesogloea*. The mesogloea may be thin or thick, cellular or acellular and is secreted by the epidermis and endodermis.

10. There are special stinging cells, the *cnidoblasts* which produce in them the peculiar *nematocysts* the organelles of offense and defence. About 17 types of such nematocysts have been identified.

11. Characteristic undifferentiated *interstitial cells* are found among the epidermal cells.

12. They are primitive in their lack of organs, their lack of fully differentiated epithelial and muscle cells. A muscular system consisting of contractile processes of epithelial cells.

13. Only one cavity lined with endodermal cells, is found in the body called *gastrovascular cavity.* It performs the function of digestion of food and distribution of digested food. It opens out through the mouth which opens into *stomodaeum.*

14. Mouth serves for ingestion of food as well as egestion of undigested food.

15. Digestion intracellular and intercellular.

16. There is no separate body cavity or coelom because coelom separates from alimentary canal, as found in higher Metazoa is absent. Thus these are acoelomate.

17. There is no special organelles for respiration, excretion and circulation. Respiration and excretion through general body surface by diffusion.

18. Nervous system is primitive consisting of neurons. The neurons are usually arranged as a nerve net at the base of epidermal and gastrodermal layers, and the impulse transmission tends to be radiating.

19. Sense organs may be simple or complex. In some eye-spots or statocysts are found.
20. Asexual and sexual both types of reproduction is seen. Asexual reproduction by budding. In sexual reproduction gametes are formed in gonads. Gonads are simple without any duct.
21. Cleavage holoblastic. Development indirect with a ciliated free-swimming stereogastrula, called the *planula larva.*
22. The life-history usually exhibits *metagenesis* in which free swimming sexual generation (medusa) and sedentary asexual generation (polyp) alternate with each other.

CLASSIFICATION

Phylum-Coelenterata includes about 10,000 known species. About 5000 are known as fossils. They are grouped into three classes :

Class—I Hydrozoa.

Class—II Scyphozoa.

Class—III Anthozoa.

Class-I-Hydrozoa

(Gr. *Hydro* = water, *zoon* = animal).

1. Mostly colonial and marine, a few solitary and fresh-water, sessile or free-living.
2. They are *tetramerous symmetrical* or *polymerous symmetrical.*
3. Members of this class are medusoid of polypoid or show both forms in their life-cycle.
4. Mesoglea is acellular.
5. Nematocysts occur only in the epidermis.
6. Gametes develop in the epidermis.
7. Hydromedusae are usually small and planktonic.
8. The asexual polypoid form arises from sexual medusoid form and the latter arises from the former, thus exhibiting metagenesis in the life-cycle of some hydrozoan e.g., *Obelia.*
9. Naked solitary species e.g., hydras probably stem from early polypoid forms which were not colonial.
10. Associated with colonial organization have been the evolution of a skeleton (support) and division of labour (Polymorphism).
11. Zygote undergoes complete cleavage and a hollow blastula is formed which changes into a solid *stereogastrula* whose ectodermal cells acquire cilia and then this stereogastrula changes into free-swimming

planula. Planula settles down, attaches by its anterior end to a substratum and by budding forms the branched colonial polypoid stage.

The class Hydrozoa is divided into five orders :

Order (i) Hydroida

1. Solitary or colonial.
2. The polyps are more developed.
3. Medusoid stage present or absent.
4. Sense organs of medusae are exclusively ectodermal.

It is divided in following sub-orders :

Suborder (a) Anthomedusae or Athecata

1. Skeletal covering, when present, does not surround hydrotheca. Freshwater or marine.
2. Polyps are naked.
3. Medusae are bud or bell-shaped. The gonads are situated on the manubrium, Statocysts absent.

   Examples : *Hydra, Protohydra, Bougainvillea, Tubularia, Hydractinia* etc.

Suborder (b) Leptomedusae or Thecata

1. Usually marine.
2. Hydranth surrounded by a theca.
3. Medusa flattened, bowl shaped. Gonads are present on the radial canals. Eye-spot and statocysts are present.

   Examples : *Obelia, Sertularia, Plumularia, Aglaophenia* etc.

Suborder (c) Limnomedusae

1. Polypoid stage without perisarcal skeleton.
2. Some only with medusoid stage

   Example : *Graspeda custa.*

Order (ii) Hydrocorallina

1. Polypoid generation forming a colony which secretes a massive calcareous skeleton having minute pores at the surface through which the polyps protuade.
2. Polyps dimorphic, nutritive gastrozooids and dactylozooids.

Suborder (a) Milleporina

1. Skeleton covered by only a thin epidermal layer.
2. Dactylozooids are long, hollow and with tentacles.

3. Mature medusae lead an independent life.
   Example : *Millepora.*

Suborder (b) Stylasterina

1. Dactylozooids are small, solid and without tentacles.
2. Polyps are symmetrically arranged.
3. Medusa develop in special spore-sac and never free.
   Example : *Stylaster*

Order (iii) Trachylina

1. *Medusoid* forms only, polypoid forms are absent or reduced.
2. Medusa with a velum beneath the margin of the bell and the tentacles inserted above the margin.
3. Statocysts and tentaculocysts present.
4. The planula give rise to the adult through an *actinula larva.*
   Order Trachylina is divided into two suborders :

Suborder (a) Trachymedusae

1. Senseory tentacles in pits or vesicles.
2. Gonads on radial canals.
3. Margins of bell are smooth.
   Example : *Gonionemus. Petasus.*

Suborder (b) Norcomedusae

1. Sensory tentacles not enclosed.
2. Gonads on the floor of stomach.
3. Margins of bell scalloped by tentacle bases.
   Examples : *Cunina, Polycopa.*

Order (iv) Siphonophora

1. Free floating or fee swimming colonies, showing maximum polymorphism.
2. Individuals attached to a linear stem or a circular disc.
3. A *pneumatophore* or float filled with air is present at the top in some cases.
4. Oral tentacles absent.
5. Nematocysts large and powerful.
6. Medusae incomplete, never free.
   This order is divided into two suborders :

Suborder (a) Calycophora

1. Pneumatophore is absent.

2. One or more swimming zooids are present in the upper part of the colony.

    Examples : *Abyla, Diphyses, Praya.*

Suborder (b) Physophorida

1. A large pneumatophore is present at the upper end of the colony.
2. Zooids are polypoid and medusoid.

    Examples : *Physalia, Halistemma.*

Order (v) Choandrophora

1. Pelagic, polymorphic, polypoid colony with a gas filled float.
2. There is a central gastrozooid surrounded by many gonozooids.
3. Dactylozoids arranged in a marginel circlet.

    Examples : *Porpita, Velella.*

Class-II Scyphozoa

1. Class Scyphozoa include large jelly fishes.
2. Polyp satge is usually reduced or absent.
3. Medusa are large, umbrella-shaped without velum. Perisarc is absent.
4. The sense organs are in the form of hollow *tentaculocysts* having statolith.
5. The gastral tentacles are endodermal.
6. Mesogloea enlarged and usually cellular.
7. The gonads are endodermal and release the gametes in stomach.
8. Stomodaeum is absent in the gastro-vascular system but gastric tentacles are present and the cavity is divided into interradial pockets by four ridges or speta.
9. Alternation of generation is seen in some.
10. They are exclusively marine.

    The class is divided into 5 orders.

Order (i) Lucernarida

1. Mostly found in cold littoral waters.
2. Sessile and sedentary, attached to the substratum by the aboral stalk.
3. Body is goblet or trumpet shaped.
4. Mouth is four cornered with small oral lobes and a short manubrium.
5. Tentacles are present in some, they are per-radial and inter-radial.
6. The umbrella is cup-shaped.
7. Gonads are long band-shaped lying on faces of septa.

8. Larva is planula with cilia.

Examples : *Lucernaria, Haliclystus.*

Order (ii) Coronatae

1. Free swimming forms living in deep sea.
2. Body conical or dome-shaped divided into an upper cone and lower crown by a coronary groove.
3. Solid tentacles are per-radial and ad-radial, 4 interradial *rhopalina* present.
4. Four to sixteen tentaculocysts.

Examples : *Pericolpa, Atolla.*

Order (iii) Cubomedusae

1. Free-swimming found in warm and shallow waters.
2. The umbrella is four-sided and cup-shaped.
3. Four hollow inter-radial tentacles and four per-radial tentaculocysts are present. Each tentaculocyst with one or more ocelli and a lithocyst.
4. A true velum is absent.
5. Gonads are leaf-like and there is no alternation of generation in life-cycle.

Examples : *Chiropsalmus, Tamoya.*

Order (iv) Semaeostomae

1. Common free-swimming animals found all over the world.
2. The umbrella is disc-like.
3. Mouth surrounded by four oral arms.
4. Eight or more tentaculocysts are present.
5. Gastric pouches and septa are absent.

Examples : *Aurelia, Cyanea.*

Order (v) Rhizostomae

1. Free-swimming forms found is shallow waters of tropical and subtropical oceans.
2. The mouth is obliterated by the growth across it of 8 very large and branched oral arms.
3. The stomach is continued into the canals opening by funnel shaped apertures on the edges of the arms.
4. Umbrella is saucer or bowl-shaped.
5. Marginal tentacles absent.
6. Tentaculocysts are 8 or more in number.

Examples : *Rhizostoma, Cassiopeia.*

Class-III Anthozoa or Actinozoa

1. Exist only in the polyp form, no medusa stage.
2. Differ from hydrozoan and scyphozoan polyp in possessing a stomodaeum, paired mesenteries (their free ends bear coiled mesenteric filaments like the gastric filaments of scyphozoan but are partially ectodermal in origin).
3. Body wall consists of ectoderm and endoderm separated by a strong mesogloea having fibres and cells.
4. Stomodacum consists of the same layers reversed i.e., its lining membrane is ectodermal. The mesenteries are formed by a double layer of endoderm with a supporting plate of mesogloea.
5. More complex nematocysts than in Hydrozoa and Scyphozoa are found in the tentacles, body-wall, stomodacum and mesenteric filaments.
6. Muscular system is well-developed containing both ectodermal and endodermal fibres and endodermal muscule processes.
7. Nervous system is a typical nerve net.
8. Gonads develop in the mesenteries, sex cells are located in the endoderm, and sperms and ova are discharged into the coelenteron.
9. The zygote develops into a planula which after swimming freely for sometime settles down and metamorphoses into the adult form.
10. Except in one doubtful instance there is no alternation of generations.

The class-Anthozoa is divided into 2 sub-classes :

Subclass-1. Hexacorallina or Zoantharia

1. Solitary or colonial marine forms.
2. Tentacles and mesenteries very numerous, arranged in multiple of six.
3. Tentacles are simple, unbranched, hollow cones.
4. Two siphonoglyphs are present and two pairs of directive mesenteries; the remaining mesenteries are generally arranged in couples with the longitudinal muscles of each couple facing one another.

Order (i) Actiniaria

1. The animals are commonly called sea-anemones. They are solitary or colonial, brightly coloured.
2. Tentacles and mesenteries are numerous.
3. Skeleton is absent.
4. One or more siphonoglyphs.

Examples : *Metridium, Adamsia, Edwardsia*.

Order (ii) Madreporaria

1. The animals are usually colonial.
2. Skeleton is external and calcareous.
3. Siphonoglyph is absent.
4. Polyps are very small.
5. These are stony corals.

   Examples : *Corallium, Madrepora, Fungia, Meandra, Favia.*

Order (iii) Zoanthidea

1. Mostly colonial and some are solitary forms.
2. The tentacles are unbranched.
3. The skeleton is usually of a calcareous nature but in few cases there is a horny axial skeleton.
4. Polyps are small and often united by basal stolons.
5. Mesentries paired. Each pair with a complete and an incomplete mesentery.
6. They have single siphonoglyph.

   Example : *Zoanthus.*

Order (iv) Antipatharia

1. These are compound tree-like animals. Commonly known as *black corals.*
2. The tentacles and mesenteries are comparatively few (6-24) in number.
3. The skeleton is present in the form of a branched chitinoid axis.
4. Two siphonoglyphs.

   Example : *Antipathes.*

Order (v) Ceriantharia

1. The individuals are long and solitary.
2. Skeleton is absent.
3. The mesenteries are incomplete.
4. Numerous, simple tentacles are arranged in two wholrs-oral and marginal.
5. There is a single dorsal siphonoglyph.

   Example : *Cerianthus, Pachycerianthus.*

Order (vi) Corallimorpharia

1. Solitary or colonial polyps without skeleton.
2. Radially arranged tentacles.

   Example : *Corynactis.*

Subclass-2 Octocorallina

1. Colonial marine forms.

2. Only polyps no medusae.
3. Tentacles and mesenteries always eight in number.
4. The tentacles pinnate; i.e., produced into symmetrical branchlets.
5. Never more than one siphonoglyph, which is ventral in position, i.e., faces the proximal end of the colony.
6. The arrangement of mesenteries is not always in couples (or pairs) and all their longitudinal muscles are directed ventrally i.e., towards the same side as the siphonoglyph.

This subclass is divided into following orders :

Order (i) Stolonifera
1. Found in shallow waters.
2. Polyps arising form a creeping stolon.
3. Skeleton either absent or of calcareous tubes or separate calcareous spicules.
4. Found on coral-reefs in Old and New World.

Examples : *Tubipora, Clavularia.*

Order (ii) Telestacea
1. Colony formed of simple or branched stems arising from a creeping base.
2. Skeleton of calcareous spicules.

Example : *Telesto.*

Order (iii) Alcyonacea
1. The skeleton usually consists of calcareous spicules or the spicules become aggregated so as to form a coherent skeleton.
2. Some forms may be dimorphic.
3. Body is branched with a central axis.
4. Polyps embedded in fleshy coenochyme.

Examples : *Alcyonium, Gersemia.*

Order (iv) Coenothecalia
1. Blue or brown corals found on coral reefs in the Indo-Pacific waters.
2. Skeleton massive, calcareous and blue-green formed from iron salts.

Example : *Heliopora.*

Order (v) Gorgonacea
1. The individuals are compound tree-like.
2. Skeleton is calcareous or horny.
3. Spicules are present in mesogloea.

4. Siphonoglyph is absent.

5. A central skeletal axis composed of a horn-like substance, the *gorgonin*.
   Examples : *Gorgonia, Corallium.*

Order (vi) Pennatulacea

1. The colony is usually elongated.

2. One end of the colony remains embeded in the mud at the sea-bottom
   while other end bears the polyps.

3. The rachis is the axial polyp bearing numerous dimorphic polyps
   laterally.

4. The skeleton is calcareous or horny.

   Examples : *Pennatula, Renilla, Pteroeides.*

SERTULARIA

Phylum	-	Coelenterata
Class	-	Hydrozoa
Order	-	Hydroida
Suborder	-	Leptomedusae
Genus	-	*Sertularia*

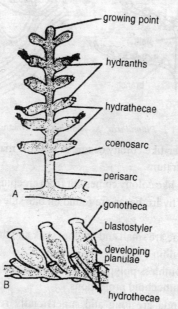

Fig. 1.1. *Sertularia* A—Branch with hydranths B—Branch with gonands.

1. It is a small branching colony occurs in shallow marine water on submerged objects or rocks.
2. Hydrotheca sessile i.e., not stalked, with *opercula* in pair along the stem being exactly opposite to each other.
3. Hydrothecae are large, polyps retract within themselves.
4. *Gonangia* are of simple form, much larger than hydrothecae, a few in a colony and present only in a certain period of three years.
5. Blastostyles produce *planulae* and no free medusae.

PLUMULARIA

The classification is the same as that of *Sertularia*.

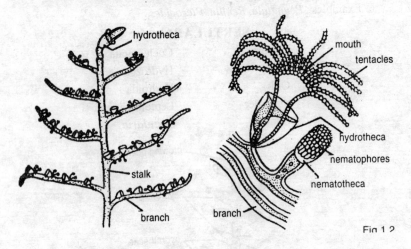

Fig. 1.2. *Plumularia.* A—Coloney B—Magnified polpy.

1. It is a feather-like colony occurs in shallow marine water attached to some substratum.
2. The plume-like colony comes out from creeping hydrorhiza.
3. A series of hydrothecae are found on one side of the branches of the colony.
4. Hydrothecae are small and without stalk and the polyps can be partly retracted within them.
5. Special mouthless polyps known as *nematophores* are found which have long amoeboid projections.
6. The gonangia are long and superficially resembling the spadix inflorescence.

CLYTIA

The systematic position is same as that of *Sertularia.*

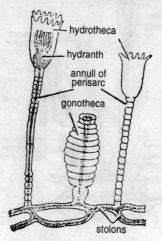

Fig. 1.3. *Clytia.*

1. It forms a simple or sparsely branched colony attached to docks, algae etc. in shallow sea water.
2. The hydrocaulus are long, more or less annulated and rising separately from the hydrorhiza
3. Hydranths are located in the hydrothecae. The margins of hydrothecae are toothed.
4. Hydranth bear several filiform tentacles around the hypostome.
5. The gonotheca is annulated, sessile and develops on the hydrorhiza or the stem.
6. The medusae when liberated, bear brown gonads a short manubrium with four small oral lobes, 16 tentacles and 16 lithocysts.

CAMPANULARIA

Phylum	-	Coelenterata
Class	-	Hydrozoa
Order	-	Hydroida
Suborder	-	Leptomedusae
Genus	-	*Campanularia*

1. It is a simple branched colony found attached to submerged marine objects in shallow water.

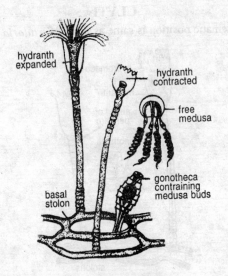

Fig. 1.4. *Campanularia.*

2. Hydrothecae, enclosing polyps, are bell-shaped usually stalked, without operculum and with or without marginal teeth.

3. Annulated stem at the base of the branch.

4. *Blastostyle* produces *planulae* and not medusae.

5. *Gonanagium* long and slender.

6. Hypostome of hydranth or polyp tumpet - shaped surrounded by tentacles.

HYDRACTINIA

Phylum	-	Coelenterata
Class	-	Hydrozoa
Order	-	Hydroida
Suborder	-	Anthomedusae
Genus	-	*Hydractinia*

1. It is a small, marine hydroid found in shallow water attached to stones, sea-weeds and shells.

2. It is commonly found on Atlantic coast, U.S.A., Europe and also found in Sanjuan Island.

3. Zooids are of four types *gastrozooid* (feeding polyp), *gonozooid* (reproductive zooid), *dactylozooid* (protective zooid) and *tentaculozooid* (sensory polyp).

4. The hydranths are simply mouthless and are called as dactylozooids.

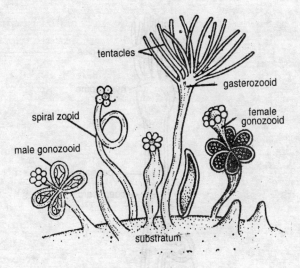

Fig. 1.5. *Hydractinia.*

5. The dectylozooids have very short tentacles abundantly supplied with nematocysts.

6. The dactylozooids are capable of very active movements.

7. With the help of massive coenosarc consisting of a number of branches, *Hydractinia* form a firm brownish crust on the surfaces of dead gatropod shells inhabited by hermit-crabs.

8. The association between *Hydractinia* and hermit carbs is known as *commensalism.*

9. The hydroid feed upon minute fragments of the hermit crab's food and the hermitcrab is protected from its enemies by the presence of the inedible stinging hydroid.

EUDENDRIUM

The systematic position is same as that of *Hydractinia.*

1. *Eudendrium* forms a branching colony arising from a reticulated hydrorhiza.

2. Perisarc is well distinct and variously annulated.

3. Hydranth has a trumped-like hypostome.

4. The hypostome is surrounded by a whorl of filiform tentacles.

5. Free medusae are absent. There occurs an intermediate stage between *Obelia* and *Bougainvillea.*

6. The medusae are budded off from the stalk of a polyp which loses its
   ′ tentacles, diminishes in length and becomes a blastostyle.

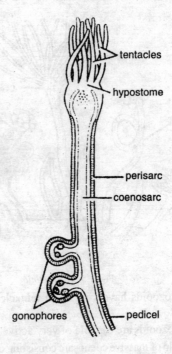

Fig. 1.6. *Eudendrium.*

7. Male and female gonophores develop on the same colony.

8. Male sporosacs occur in a whorl just beneath, and the female sporosacs usually just above the tentacles and occasionally on the hydrocaulus.

9. The male sporosacs are reddish and arranged in monoliform bundles, while female sporosacs are orange in colour and are pyriform. Each female sporosac bears a single ovum attached above the tentacles.

CERATELLA

Classification is the same as that of *Hydractinia.*

1. It is a colonial, sedentary hydroid coelenterate.

2. It is tree-like highly branched animal.

3. It consists of a branching axis composed of many inter-twisting and anastomosing tubes.

4. Hydrotheca covers polyp while gonotheca covers medusa.

5. The zooids have scattered capitate tentacles.

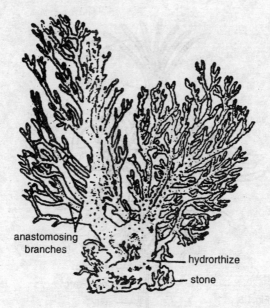

anastomosing
branches

hydrorthize

stone

Fig. 1.7. *Ceratella.*

6. The medusae bear gonads on the manubrium and devoid of lithocytes.
7. Eye spots are present.

TUBULARIA

The systematic position of *Tubularia* is same as that of *Hydractinia*.

1. It is a marine hydroid occuring solitary or in large pink colonies attached to substratum.
2. The colony consists of tufts of irregularly branched stems bearing hydranths arising from hydrorhiza.
3. The hydranths are large in size and bright in colour, with a flower-like appearance.
4. Each hydranth consists of a proximal narrow neck attaching it to the stem and a distal larger conical region bearing two whorls of solid, filiform tentacles.
5. The distal smaller tentacles arise from the hypostome surrounding the mouth.
6. The basal tentacles are large and surround the base of hydranth.
7. At the base of hydranth, the stalk forms a swelling where the perisarc comes to an end without forming a protective hydrotheca around the hydranth.

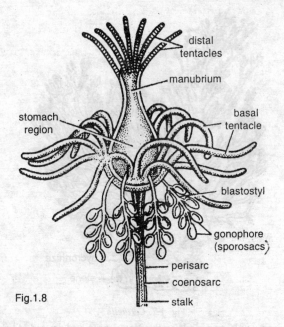

Fig. 1.8. *Tubularia.*

8. The stalk or stem contains perisarc and coenosarc and is transparent.

9. The gonophores or sporosacs arise as hollow branches from the body of hydranth between two sets of tentacles. Gonophores produce medusae.

10. The colony is dioecious with separate male and female members.

11. The medusae are deep bell-shaped with manubrial gonads and four knob-like tentacles. The medusae are not set free. The fertilized eggs remain in the female gonophore.

12. Development is indirect with a *planula larva* never becomes free swimming, but metamorphoses into a polypoid, tentaculate *actinula larva* which is then set-free.

13. Asexual reproduction by budding.

BOUGAINVILLEA

The classification is the same as that of *Hydractinia.*

1. It is a plant-like hydroid colony inhabiting in sea waters.

2. Two types of zooids are present the *polyp* or *hydranth* and *medusa.*

3. Polyps are vegetative responsible for nutrition and food catching, while medusa is reproductive in function.

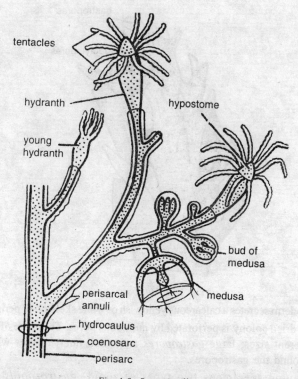

tentacles

hydranth

young
hydranth

hypostome

bud of
medusa

perisarcal
annuli

medusa

hydrocaulus

coenosarc

perisarc

Fig. 1.9. *Bougainvillea.*

4. Hydrotheca and gonotheca coverings are absent on polyp and medusa respectively.

5. Polyp is beset with a single circlet of filiform tentacles which surround the hypostome.

6. Medusa bears four radial canals and a wide velum.

7. On the manubrium of medusa develops the gonads.

MILLEPORA

Phylum	-	Coelenterata
Class	-	Hydrozoa
Order	-	Hydrocorallina
Suborder	-	Milliporina
Genus	-	*Millepora*

1. Marine colonial form found in tropical seas and associated with other corals.

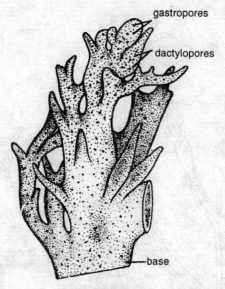

gastropores

dactylopores

base

Fig. 1.10. *Millepora.*

2. Ectoderm secretes a calcareous yellowish or white skeleton of perisarc.

3. The dried colony is perforated by numerous pores. These are of two different sizes; large *gastropores* and small *dactylopores* which surround the gastropores.

4. In living specimens two types of zooid- *gastrozooids* and *dactylozooids* which protude out of these pores.

5. Gastrozooids are feeding zooids, having 4-5 short knobbed tentacles. The dactylozooids are protective zooids with capitate tentacles having nematocysts.

6. Pores lead into canals which forms network in coenosarc.

7. Medusae with 4 or 5 rudimentary tentacles. These are free, simple and originate from coenosarc.

STYLASTER

Phylum	-	Coelenterata
Class	-	Hydrozoa
Order	-	Hydrocorallina
Suborder	-	Stylasterina
Genus	-	*Stylaster*

1. It is highly branched, tree-like, deep pink colony found in tropical and subtropical seas.

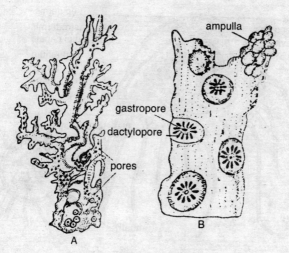

Fig. 1.11. *Stylaster.*

2. Numerous upright branches of calcium carbonate are present.

3. On the branches are cup-shaped projections formed of several zooids.

4. *Gastrozooids* situated in the centre, while *dactylozooids* are in the periphery.

5. *Gonophores* or reproductive zooids are lodged in a special chamber or *ampulla* of the coral.

6. Form the horizontal partition at the bottom of each cup projects a calcareous projection callled *style*, hence the generic name *Stylaster* is given.

7. The young sets free in the planula stage which later on metamorphoses into a new colony.

GONIONEMUS

Phylum	-	Coelenterata
Class	-	Hydrozoa
Order	-	Trachylina
Suborder	-	Trachymedusae
Genus	-	*Gonionemus*

1. It is a medusa found in bottom of sea water. It is cosmopolitan in distribution.

2. It is like the medusa of *Obelia* and generally bell-like or saucer shaped.

3. The convex outer surface of the bell is known as exumbrella while the concave inner surface is subumbrella.

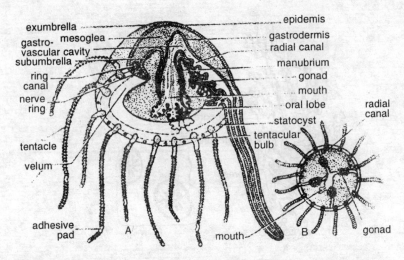

Fig. 1.12. *Gonionemus*. A—Section to show internal structure, B—Sub-umbrellar side.

4. From the centre of the concave or subumbrella surface hangs down a short, hollow and quardrangular process known as the *manubrium* bearing four brief frilled oral lobes surrounding the mouth.

5. The rim of the margin of the medusa bears numerous 16 to 18 highly contractile tentacles provided with belts of nematocysts and adhesive pads.

6. The adhesive pads are generally situated at the bending on each tentacle and helps in anchoring to marine plant at rest.

7. The gonads are situated on four radial canals and medusae are unisexual.

8. Planula develops into small polyp which has mouth tentacles and is known as *haleremite*.

9. The haleremite reproduces asexually and gives rise to planula-like buds which are nonciliated and are called *frustules*.

10. The frustules develop into new polyps which from external side bud off gonophores. These naked gonophores give rise to medusae.

DIPHYES

Phylum	-	Coelenterata
Class	-	Hydrozoa
Order	-	Siphonophora
Suborder	-	Calycophora
Genus	-	*Diphyes*

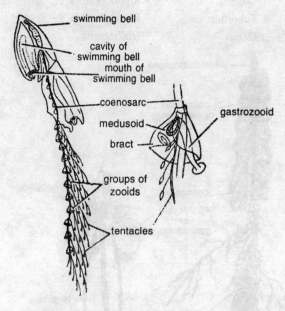

Fig. 1.13. *Diphyes.* A—Entire colony; B—Single group of zooids.

1. It is a polymorphic colonial, marine and pelagic coelenterate.
2. It has cosmopolitan distribution.
3. Pneumatophore is absent.
4. The colony consists of a coenosarcal stem bearing groups of zooids called *cormidia* and two large swimming bells or *nectophores*. The bells are present at the proximal end of colony.
5. Below the nectophores, the stem bears widely separated groups of zooids. These can be retracted into a groove in nectophores.
6. Other zooids attached to the bells are tentacles bearing gastrozooids, a medusa and a large bract of protective nature.
7. Each group of zooid (Cormidium) consists of a hydrophyllium, a gastrozooids with its tentacles and a gonozoid.
8. The stem often breaks at the inter-nodes. Detached zooids are called *endoxia*, which swim about like independent organisms and become sexually mature.

HALISTEMMA

Phylum	-	Coelenteraia
Class	-	Hydrozoa

Order   -   Siphonophora
Suborder   -   Physophorida
Genus   -   *Halistemma*

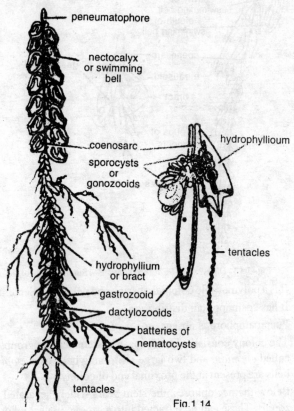

Fig. 1 14

Fig. 1.14. *Halistemma.* A—Coloney, B—Cormidium.

1. It is a polymorphic colony found floating on the surface of Mediterranean sea.

2. Uppermost end of the stem possesses an ovid bubble-like body, known as *float* or *pneumatophore* containing air.

3. Below the penumatophore, there is a series of unsymmetrical medusae, called *nectocalyces* each having a deep bell-like body with a velum and without manubrium.

4. *Swimming bells* or *nectocalyces* contract, drawing water into their cavities and pumping it out to propel the whole organism through water.

5. Stem underneath divides into nodes and internodes.
6. Below certain nodes arise *polyps* with a long, branched tentacle and bearing batteries of *"stinging capsule"*.
7. In the remaining nodes, *dactylozooides* or *feelers* take the place of polyps.
8. Below these dactylozooids are *sporosacs*, some are males and others females.
9. Delicate leaf-like, transparent bodies, the bracts or *hydrophylia*, spring from internodes.

PHYSALIA

Phylum	-	Coelenterata
Class	-	Hydrozoa
Order	-	Siphonophora
Suborder	-	Physophorida
Genus	-	*Physalia*

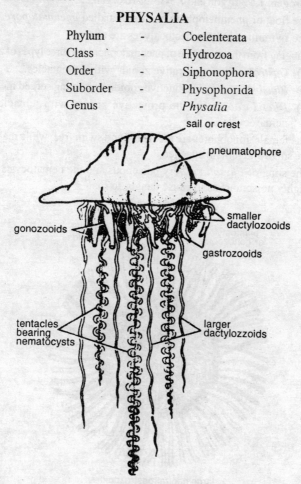

Fig. 1.15. *Physalia*

1. It is a marine, pelagic, polymorphic hydroid.
2. It is found in the gulf stream from Florida to Vineyard Sound and occasionally to the Bay of Fundy.
3. It is commonly called '*Portuguese man of war*', because it has a large, brilliant coloured pneumatophore or float which is like the cap of Great Napolean.
4. The dorsal side of float is called *crest* or *sail*.
5. The float is filled with a gas. The composition of the gas is 85-91% nitrogen, 1.5% argon and 7.5-13.5% oxygen.
6. The float or pneumetophore has a pore called *pneumatopore*.
7. The swimming bells or nectocalyces are absent.
8. Hanging from the underside of pneumatophore are three types of zooids:
   (i) *Gastrozooids* are nutrative zooids without tentacles.
   (ii) *Blastostyles* are reproductive zooids containing served medusae.
   (iii) *Dactylozooids* are the protective zooids with tentacles and nematocysts.
9. The female gonophores are medusoid and swim free, while male ones are small and remain attached.
10. The sting of *Physalia* is very poisonous and the nematocysts are so highly poisonous as to cause danger to man.

PORPITA

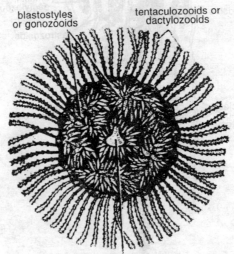

Fig. 1.16. *Porpita.*

The classification is the same as that of *Physalia*.

1. *Porpita* is a marine coelenterate found usually on South Atlantic Coast and occasionally near U.K. Coast.
2. The float is very large, circular and disc like (like the float of *Physalia*).
3. The colony consists of disc-like body enclosing a chambered chitinoid shell.
4. It exhibits the remarkable phenomenon of *polymorphism*.
5. Long dactylozooids or tentacles are present around the disc.
6. The under-surface is beset with gonozooids or blastostyles provided with mouth bearing the medusae.
7. The single gastrozooid is present in the centre of disc on ventral side as in *Velella*.
8. Crest is wanting.

VELELLA

The classification is the same as that of *Physalia*.

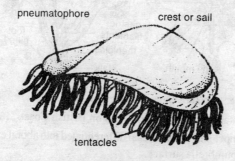

Fig. 1.17. *Velella.*

1. It is a beautifully coloured pelagic form found in warm water. It is common is Pacific Coast and South Atlantic Coast.
2. Body rhomboidal with a medusa-like appearnce.
3. Pneumatophore dorsal, in the form of a chambered chitinous disc and bears a vertical crest like ridges.
4. Hanging from the centre of the under surface is a single large gastrozooid which is surrounded by numerous gonozooids which give off medusa-buds.
5. The gonozooids are devoid of tentacles.
6. Dactylozooids hang down from the rim of the disc forming a circular fringe.

7. It is incapable of sinking down by altering the gas contents of the float.

LUCERNARIA

Phylum	-	Coelenterata
Class	-	Scyphozoa
Order	-	Lucermnarida
Genus	-	*Lucernaria*

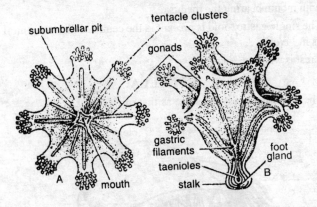

Fig. 1.18. *Lucernaria.* A—Oral view, B—Side view.

1. It is a sedentary, sessile animal found on British Coast.
2. Body is trumpet-shaped or conical differentiated into aboral exumbrella and oral subumbrella surface.
3. Exumbrella surface drawn out into a short, cylindrical stalk used for attachment to sea-weeds.
4. Margin of umbrella drawn into 8 short and hollow adhesive lobes or adradial arms.
5. Each arm bears a cluster of knobbed adhesive tentacles.
6. Mouth is cruciform (four cornered) with small oral lobes and a short manubrium.
7. Gastrovascular system consists of central stomach and four perradial pouches divided by four interradial septa.
8. Gastric filaments numerous.
9. Gonals are band-like brone on septa.
10. Marginal adhesive gastric pits and velum are absent.

CHARYBDAEA

Phylum	-	Coelenterata
Class	-	Scyphozoa
Order	-	Cubomedusae
Genus	-	*Charybdaea*

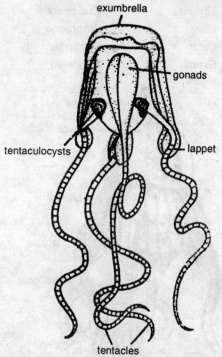

Fig. 1.19. *Charybdaea.*

1. It is a marine animal. It is commonly found in the warm shallow waters of tropical and subtropical region.
2. It is an active swimmer and swims through the water appearing beautiful.
3. It resembles a deep bell with somewhat flattened top and square in transverse section.
4. The margin of the umbrella bears 4 tentacles and 4 tentaculocysts.
5. The tentacles are inter-radial and tentaculocysts are per-radial.
6. The tentaculocysts are set in deep marginal notches and the tentacles arise from gelatinous lobes.
7. The tentaculocysts are very complex, each bearing a lithocyst and several eye-spots.

8. The margin of the umbrella is produced into a false velum like the velarium of *Aurelia*.

9. The nervous system is present in the form of nerve ring round the margin of bell.

PERICOLPA

Phylum	-	Coelenterata
Class	-	Scyphozoa
Order	-	Coronatae
Genus	-	*Pericolpa*

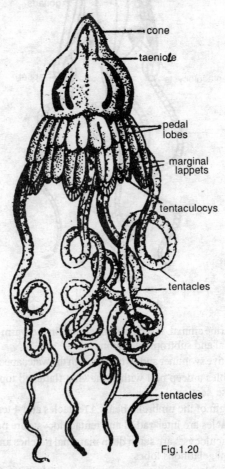

Fig.1.20

Fig. 1.20. *Paricolp*

1. It is a beautiful marine solitary medusoid animal.
2. It is cosmopolitan is distribution, but abundent found in Greenland.
3. Umbrella is divided into apical cone and marignal crown by a furrow.
4. Marginal crown is divided into a series of pedal lobes and series of marginal lappets by a second horizontal furrow.
5. Marginal lappets and pedal lobes are present in same radii.
6. Tentaculocysts are present on four interradial pedal lobes.
7. Large mouth opens into the stomach by manubrium.

CYANEA

Phylum	-	Coelenterata
Class	-	Scyphozoa
Order	-	Semaeostomae
Genus	-	*Cyanea*

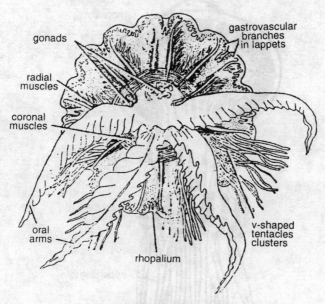

Fig. 1.21. *Cyanea.*

1. It is the largest, solitary, bioluminescent and marine medusa.
2. It is found in the costal waters of America, Pacific Coast and Polar Regions.
3. It is commonly called as '*sun-jelly*' or '*sea-blubber*'.
4. Umbrella dome-shaped or saucer-shaped with margin scalloped into eight lappets having eight rhopalia.

5. Subumbrella carries four long oral arms and eight V-shaped bundles of tentacles, the marginal tentacles.
6. Four gonads, placed between oral arms and tentacles.
7. Circular canal absent. Radial canals branch profusely and extend into rhopalia and tentacles are present.
8. It produces burning sensation.

RHIZOSTOMA

Phylum	-	Coelenterata
Class	-	Scyphozoa
Order	-	Rhizostomae
Genus	-	*Rhizostoma*

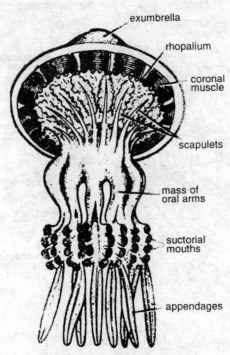

exumbrella

rhopalium

coronal muscle

scapulets

mass of oral arms

suctorial mouths

appendages

Fig. 1.22. *Rhizostoma.*

1. It is an inhabitant of shallow water in tropical and subtropical zones, sometimes, in temperate zones. These are also found in Indo-Pacific Region and North Carolina.

2. The colour varies. The colour of umbrella is pale green with a deep reddish margin, arms bright blue.
3. The marginal tentacles are absent.
4. The orignal four arms become divided longitudinally into eight.
5. The mouth is one is young but it is replaced by numerous small "sucking mouths" in adult which lie along the lips.
6. Lips act as organs for external digestion.
7. It feeds upon small animals like fishes etc.
8. The mesogloea of the medusae of *Rhizostoma* is neither gelatinous nor mucilaginous. The entire medusa contains 91 to 96% water content.
9. The umbrella is about 2 feet in length and specimen is about 4 feet.

EDWARDSIA

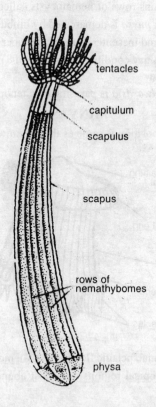

tentacles

capitulum

scapulus

scapus

rows of nemathybomes

physa

Fig. 1.23. *Edwardsia.*

Phylum	-	Coelenterata
Class	-	Anthozoa
Subclass	-	Hexacorallina
Order	-	Actiniaria
Genus	-	*Edwardsia*

1. It is a small, solitary, marine animal, burries in sand. It is found in U.S.A., Southern California and North of Cape Cod.
2. Body is elongated and is diffrentiated into oral disc and column.
3. Oral disc is short and carries centrally placed mouth and a circlet of 16 tentacles arranged in two rows.
4. The cylindrical column has three parts, the *capitulum, scapulus* and *scapus.*
5. The body surface has 8 longitudinal ridges and the posterior half of the scapus contains rows of nematocysts called as *nemathybomes.*
6. The basal part or *physa* is demarcated by limbus from scapus.
7. Siphonoglyphs and mesenteris are 8 in number are present.
8. Septa are in primitive condition consisting of 8 macrosepta and more than 4 microsepta.
9. The young of *Edwardsia* is parasitic on Ctenophore.

MINYAS

The systematic position is same as that of *Edwardsia.*

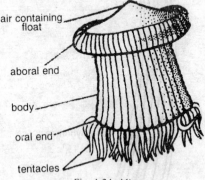

air containing float

aboral end

body

oral end

tentacles

Fig. 1.24. *Minyas.*

1. *Minyas* is a colonial, pelagic floating sea-anemone.
2. It is found in tropical regions and most abundant in shallow and costal waters.
3. It is a blue coloured anthozoan.

4. The oral disc bears a large number of tentacles.
5. The column is short.
6. Skeleton is absent.
7. The basal disc contains an air-filled sac, due to which the animal floats.
8. The mesenteries are arranged in the multiple of six. The siphonoglyphs are present.

CERIANTHUS

Phylum	-	Coelenterata
Class	-	Anthozoa
Subclass	-	Hexacorallina
Order	-	Ceriantharia
Genus	-	*Cerianthus*

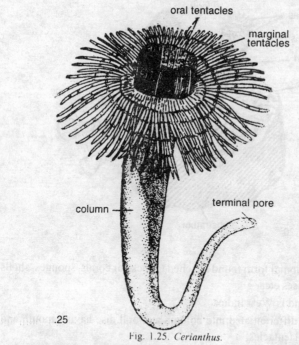

Fig. 1.25. *Cerianthus.*

1. It is found along the Pacific and Atlantic Coasts, Cape Cod to Florida, Bay of Fundy and Mediterranean.
2. The form resembles a sea anemone and has cylindrical elongated body but without pedal disc.

3. The oral region has numerous tentacles about 130 arranged in 2 rows, the marginal whorl of tentacles and inner circlet of tentacles.

4. The lower end is round and has terminal pore.

5. Pharynx has only one siphonoglyph.

6. The ectoderm secretes in long tube of mucus in which the animal lives and the tube is fixed in soft, sandy or muddy sea bottom.

7. On the tube sand particles are deposited so it becomes hard.

ZOANTHUS

Phylum	-	Coelenterata
Class	-	Anthozoa
Subclass	-	Hexacorallina
Order	-	Zoantheria
Genus	-	*Zoanthus*

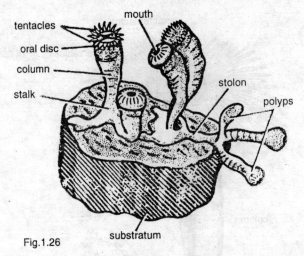

Fig.1.26

Fig. 1.26. *Zoanthus.*

1. It is a colonial form found attached to rocks or corals, sponges, shells of molluscs etc.

2. It is found is West Indies.

3. Body is differentiated into column and oral disc having mouth and marginal tentacles.

4. Cylindrical, small polyps arise singly from a network of stolon.

5. Tentacles are numerous, 48-60 in number arranged in one or two rows.

6. Mesenteries paired consisting of both micro- and macro-mesenteries.

7. Single siphonoglyph is present.

8. Sexes are separate and asexual reproduction by budding.

MADREPORA

Phylum	-	Coelenterata
Class	-	Anthozoa
Subclass	-	Hexacorallina
Order	-	Madreporaria
Genus	-	*Madrepora*

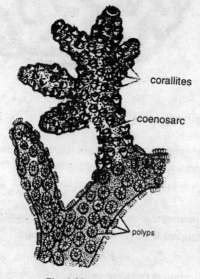

corallites

coenosarc

polyps

Fig. 1.27. *Madrepora.*

1. It is a colonial, symbiotic and marine coral found in West Indies and Florida.

2. It is commonly called as '*horn coral*' and plays an important role in coral-reef formation.

3. Colony is branched with numerous, small crowded polyps in elevated cylindrical cups separated by coenosteum.

4. Terminal polyps contain 6 tentacles and lateral polyps with 12 tentacles.

5. Internally mesentries are bilaterally arranged and coenosarc contains a network of canals.

6. Sometimes small crustaceans are found in association with horny corals.

MEANDRINA

The classification is the same as that of *Madrepora*.

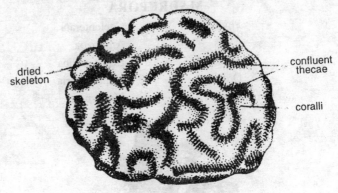

dried skeleton

confluent thecae

coralli

Fig. 1.28. *Meandrina*.

1. Colonial form inhibiting the coastal waters of West India, Asia and America.
2. It is popularly known as *brain-coral* since resembles the human brain due to the presence of long curved grooves and ridges.
3. The colony is large and is composed of lime stone secreted by ectoderm.
4. Polyps bear separate mouth, tentacular fringe, septa and mesenteries.
5. Polyps remain confluent in the living condition.

FAVIA

The classification is the same as that of *Madrepora*.

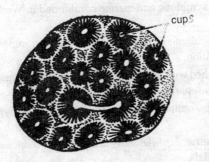

cups

Fig. 1.29. *Favia*.

1. *Favia* is a massive stony reef building coral.

2. It is commonly found in Florida and West Indies.

3. *Favia* has a compact and huge colony produced by buds.

4. The surface of the colony has closely placed polygonal cases or cups.

5. The cups are so near to each other as to have common boundaries.

6. The skeleton which is very hard, is made up of calcium carbonate material and secreted by ectoderm for support of delicate tissue.

7. The polyp is like that of sea anemones which contract in cups and are without siphonoglyph.

8. Columella present.

9. The *Favia* is aporose corals as the various parts of coral are solid and stony.

FUNGIA

The classification is the same as that of *Madrepora*.

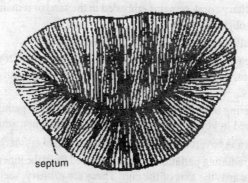

septum

Fig. 1.30. *Fungia*.

1. It is a solitary and marine coral found in warm sea, generally in Gulf of California.

2. It is commonly called '*mushroom coral*'.

3. The coral is flat and discoidal, the theca is confined to the lower surface and small calcareous rods and synapticulae, which connect septa with one another.

4. Adult animal contains a single large polyp with numerous tentacles.

5. Siphonoglyph is absent.

6. The life-history includes planula larva which metamorphoses into adult.

7. Reproduction by monodisc strobilation which are plate-like structures.

They are separated off one by one from the top of corallite. The broken discs are called *anthocyanthus* and develop into adults. The remaining broken part is called *anthocaulus* which grows again into new disc and is set off.

FLABELLUM

The systematic position is the same as that of *Madrepora*.

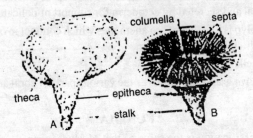

Fig. 1.31. *Flabellum curvatum,* corallite. A—Ventral view, B—Dorsal view.

1. It is a solitary coral, remains embeded in the sand or remains attached to some object.
2. The corallite forms a short conical cup or *theca*.
3. The theca is laterally compressed. It consists of dense stony calcium carbonate, rough and brownish externally but smooth and white internally.
4. The tapering base forms a short and fragile stalk for peduncle which is attached in young but may become detached when adult.
5. The theca is covered by a calcarious layer called *epitheca.*
6. Several radiating partations (Septa) proceed from the inner surface of theca towards the axis of the cup. These are primary, secondary and tertiary, like the mesenteries.
7. The primary septa meet in the centre forming the *columella* which is an irregular mass.

ASTRANGIA

The classification is the same as that of *Medrepora*.

1. It forms small encrusting colonies and found on rocks and shells— *Astrangia* is found along the coasts of Atlantic and America.
2. Colony consists of theca and polyps.
3. Polyps are white pinkish or greenish in colour.
4. Zooids are more or less isolated with six sepata of the first cycle, six smaller ones of the second and fourth cycles.

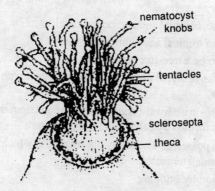

Fig. 1.32. *Astrangia.*

5. Mouth is present on the oral disc, which is surrounded by double rings of tentacles.

6. Bigger polyps have three cycles of tentacles mostly 12 larger tentacles alternating with 12 smaller tentacles.

7. It feeds on crustaceans and small fishes.

DENDROPHYLIA

The systematic position is same as that of *Madrepora.*

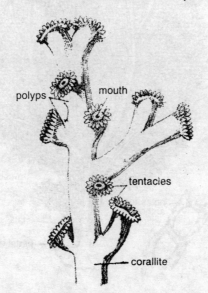

Fig. 1.33. *Dendrophylia.*

1. It is a marine, colonial and compound coral.
2. It is found in tropical and subtropical waters.
3. It appears to be a tree-like anthozoan.
4. The corallites (Polyps) do not lie in close contact with each other but are tree-like.
5. The corallites arise from a common calcareous stem or coenechyme. The stem is formed by calcification of coenosarc.
6. Each polyp possesses a centrally placed mouth which is surround by a whorl of small tentacles.
7. Reproduction by budding.

GORGONIA

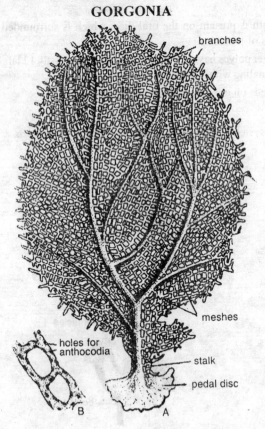

Fig. 1.34. *Gorgonia* A Coloney B a portion megnified.

Phylum	-	Coelenterata
Class	-	Actinozoa
Subclass	-	Octocorallina
Order	-	Gorgonacea
Genus	-	*Gorgonia*

1. These are present in all the seas attached to rocks and stones in shallow waters.
2. It is commonly known as '*sea-fan*'.
3. It is yellowish or brownish colony with upright branches consisting of an axial rod extending throughout the colony along all the branches.
4. The skeleton is made up of a flexible substance *gorgonin* and calcareous spicules embedded in mesogloea.
5. Polyps or anthocodia are retractile and present in rows on both the sides of the branches.
6. Sexes are separate.
7. The dried skeletons of the colony are used in decorative art.

CORALLIUM

The classification is the same as that of *Gorgonia*.

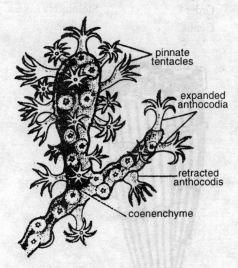

Fig. 1.35. *Corallium.*

1. It is a clonial marine animal commonly found in Mediterranean at a depth of 10-30 fathoms, Cape Verde Island, Japan, Italy etc.

2. It is commonly called '*red coral*'.
3. The colony is upright and branched and is supported by calareous axis of fused spicules.
4. The colony is dimorphic as there are two type of zooids (i) nutritive zooids, the *autozooids* and (ii) for circulation of water in the colony, the *siphonozooids*.
5. The zooids are white in colour and the colony is dark red due to the prepesence of red calcareous spicules.
6. Gonads are borne by siphonozooids.
7. Planula develops inside the zooids and so the viviparity is found in *Corallium*.
8. The *Corallium* is of great economic importance as the precious red coral of commerce known as red moonga in N. India which is obtained from this animal.

TUBIPORA

Phylum	-	Coelenterata
Class	-	Anthozoa
Subclass	-	Octocorallina
Order	-	Stolonifera
Genus	-	*Tubipora*

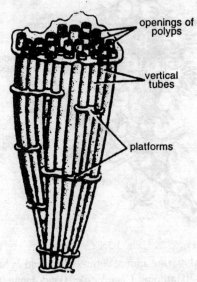

Fig. 1.36. *Tubipora*.

1. It is marine, colonial animal found in shallow waters of tropical and temperate regions.
2. It is found abudantly in shallow water of Atlantic, Indian and Pacific oceans.
3. It is commonly called '*organ pipe coral*'.
4. Colony consists of long, parallel and upright tubes closely fitted, and joined together at definite intervals by horizontal calcareous tubes.
5. The polyps are bright green and secrete these tubes.
6. The skeleton is internal and is covered by ectoderm in living condition.
7. The mesogloeal spicules become closely fitted together and form a continuous tube for each polyp.
8. Asexual reproduction by peculiar budding. The base of original polyp expands from which new polyps originate.

TELESTO

Phylum	-	Coelenterata
Class	-	Anthozoa
Subclass	-	Octocorallina
Order	-	Telestacea
Genus	-	*Telesto*

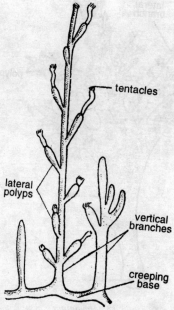

Fig. 1.37. *Telesto.*

1. It is a sedentary, marine and colonial coelenterate.
2. It is found along Atlantic coast.
3. The colony comprises simple or branched stem, which arises from a creeping base.
4. The stem bears lateral hydranths, which are arranged alternately.
5. The stem is formed by the elongation of a single polyp and the lateral originate by way of solenial networks.
6. The spicules may be somewhat united by calcareous and horny secretions.

ALCYONIUM

Phylum	-	Coelenterata
Class	-	Anthozoa
Subclass	-	Octocorallina
Order	-	Alyconacea
Genus	-	*Alcyonium*

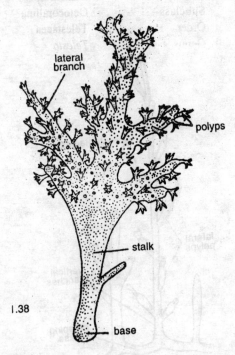

Fig. 1.38. *Alcyonium.*

1. *Alcyonium* or *Dead man's finger* is found attached to stones or rocks in sea water.
2. It has cosmpolitan distribution, but mostly found in temperate and cold water of seas. Commonly found in long Island and St. Lawrence.
3. Colony of short and thick leathery lobes attached to stones.
4. Long polyps with tentacles except those of the outer end, can be contracted and everted.
5. *Coenechcyme* (mesogloea or soft parts of an alcyonarian colony), flesh and spicules present.
6. Colour of the colony is reddish or yellowish; length is 4 to 10 cm.
7. The skeleton consists of calcareous spicules.
8. The food *(A. digitatum)* consists of various fine fragments of muscles of fish but they may reject many kinds of fish ova (according to *Pratt*).
9. Gland cells occur in stomodaeum and it is probable that they secrete a fluid for digestion.
10. The polyps are arranged on the upper part of the colony, and the lower part is sterile.

HARTEA

The systematic position is same as that of *Alcyonium*.

1. It is a marine solitary anthozoan found in shallow water.
2. The body is elongated, cylindrical. The anterior end possesses eight pinnately branched tentacles.
3. Skeleton is simplest, minute irregular deposits of calcium carbonate called spinules are deposited in the mesogloea.
4. Mouth is surrounded by the tentacles.
5. Reproduction by budding.
6. It has a simple organisation and is supposed to be persistant larval form.

HELIOPORA

Phylum	-	Coelenterata
Class	-	Anthozoa
Subclass	-	Octocorallina
Order	-	Coenothecalia
Genus	-	*Heliopora*

1. It is a marine, sedentary coral found on coral reefs in the Indo-Pacific ocean.

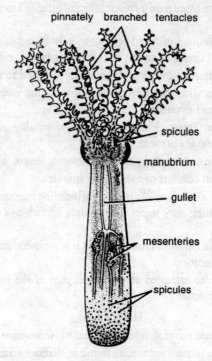

Fig. 1.39. *Hartea*.

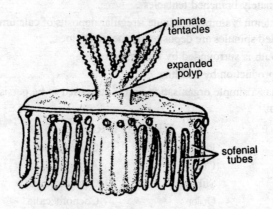

Fig. 1.40. *Heliopora*.

2. It is commonly called as '*blue coral*' because of its bright blue skeleton. The colour is due to iron salts.

3. Its massive skeleton, composed not of spicules but of crystalline fibres of arragonite fused into lamellae.

4. Skeleton is perforated by large pores through which ordinary polyps project out, and smaller pores through which siphonozooids project out.

5. It is traversed by tubular cavities of two sizes, larger cavities-few in number open out through large pores. Smaller cavities open out through small pores.

6. Surface contains flat coenechyme, which contains solonial network connected to middle region of the polyp and also with erect solonial tubes.

7. Polyps dimorphic, large ordinary zooids and small siphonozooids.

PENNATULA

Phylum	-	Coelenterata
Class	-	Anthozoa
Subclass	-	Octocorallina
Order	-	Pennatulacea
Genus	-	*Pennatula*

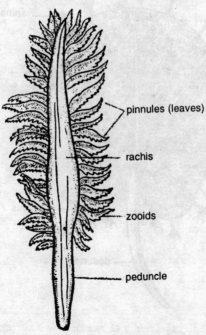

Fig. 1.41. *Pennatula.*

1. It is found fixed deep is muddy bottom of the sea. It is commonly found in Europe, South California Northward, Gulf of St. Lawrence to Carolina.
2. It is commonly called '*sea pen*'.
3. Colony is divided into two parts : (a) stalk, which is embedded in sand or mud and (b) an upper part, called the *rachis* or *horny axis*.
4. *Rachis* is elongated with paired lateral leaves or *pinnulae*.
5. Lateral leaves or pinnulae long, from 20 to 25 in number on each side.
6. Polyps, arranged on horny axis, are of two types :

   (a) *Autozooids*, whose function is nutritive, are situated side-by-side as regular lateral branches giving an appearance of a feather.
   (b) *Siphonozooids*, which maintain circulation of water in the colony, are situated on the back of the axis.

RENILLA

The classification is the same as that of *Pennatula*.

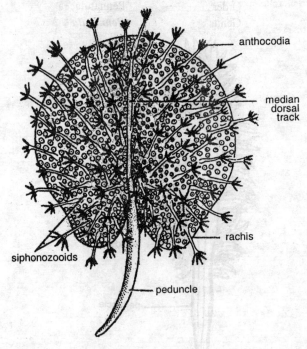

Fig. 1.42. *Renilla.*

1. It is a marine, colonial form found in shallow waters of Carolina Coast, California Coast and West Indies.

2. Colony composed of a small *peduncle* which lies embedded in the mud and a kidney-shaped *rachis*.

3. *Rachis* has a broad ventral surface devoid of polyps and a dorsal surface covered with autozooids and siphonozooids.

4. *Autozooids* or *anthocodia* lie scattered on the dorsal surface are nutritive in function.

5. *Siphonozooids* are arranged in groups and maintain the circulation of water within the colony.

6. A median bare 'track' devoid of polyps extends from the peduncle to about the middle of rachis, where it terminates at a special exhalent siphonozooid.

7. Axial skeleton absent.

VIRGULARIA

The classification is the same as that of *Pennatula*.

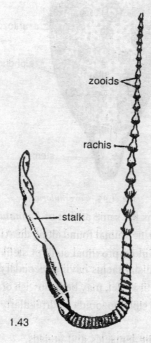

Fig. 1.43. *Virgularia.*

1. *Virgularia* or "walking stick" is found partly embedded in warmer water having a muddy and soft bottom. It is found along Pacific Coast.
2. The rachis is long and elongated like a walking stick.
3. The elongated body is divisible into two parts, *a stalk* and the *rachis*.
4. The polyps arranged in transverse rows at regular intervals and are slightly fused and arise from the *rachis*.
5. The stalk is without polyps.
6. The stalk is thrust into the muddy bottom.
7. The distal rachis stand straight outside water.

CAVERNULARIA

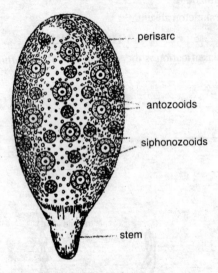

perisarc

antozooids

siphonozooids

stem

Fig. 1.44. *Cavernularia.*

The classification is the same as that of *Pennatula.*

1. It is a colonial, marine animal found along the Atlantic Coast.
2. Body is divisible into a proximal stalk or stem which is devoid of anthocodia and a distal rachis having secondary polyps.
3. The colour is blue or violet, may be yellowish or greenish.
4. Anothozooids and siphonozooids are irregularly distributed all over the rachis.
5. Anthozooids having tentacles and gonads.

6. Coenosarc is fleshy and traversed by coenosarcal canals and contains long spicules.

7. It is a bioluminescent, emits light.

Revision Questions

1. Mention the distinguishing characters of Phylum - Coelenterata and give an outline classification upto classes.

2. Classify Coelenterata up to orders giving important characters and examples.

3. Give the structure of *Millepora* or *Physalia* and *Adamsia* or *Gorgonia*.

4. Write short notes on : (a) *Porpita*, (b) *Tubipora*, (c) *Velella*, (d) *Pennatula*, (e) *Physalia*.

Hydra

Hydra belongs to the family Hydroidae and is characterized by the complete absence of perisarc and the presence of hollow tentacles. Some of the important species of *Hydra* comprise:

(i) *H. vulgaris.* Nearly colourless and common all over India. Tentacles are slender and not longer than the body.

(ii) *H. virids* (*Chlorohydra virisdissima*). It is the common green *Hydra* because of the presence of symbiotic algal organism, *Chlorella vulgaris,* in the cells of the gastral epithelium. It has not yet reported from India.

(iii) *H. fusca.* It is a pinkish yellow or brown in colour and occurs in few parts of India.

(iv) *H. gangetica.* It is commonly found in ponds along the river Ganga in India.

Hydra americana has shorter tentacles than the column *H. pseudoligactis* has distinct stalk at the basal end. *H. oligactis* lacks nipples on the testes.

The name *Hydra* was given after a mythological nine headed scaly, winged armoured fire breathing monster slain by *Hercules*.

SYSTEMATIC POSITION

Phylum	-	Coelenterata
Class	-	Hydrozoa
Order	-	Hydroida
Suborder	-	Anthomedusae
Genus	-	*Hydra*

Habits and Habitat

Hydra lives in fresh-water ponds, lakes and streams attached to submerged water plants, rocks or other objects through its adhesive basal

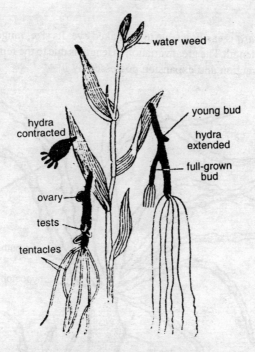

Fig. 2.1. *Hydra.* Contracted and extended.

disc. It is cosmopolitan in distribution and prefers cool, clear, permanent and stagnant water. While feeding, the body and tentacles stretch in search of food. When disturbed, the body gets contracted into a circular knob-like structure. If the animal is taken out of water, it collapses into a soft shapeless mass. It is not found in places where water is foul and the temperature is high. It is a solitary creature, though at times it may form a temporary colony by repeated budding. It is carnivorous in diet, feeding on small crustaceans, worms and insect larvae. It is itself fed by some worms and molluscs. It multiplies sexually as well as asexually.

Collection

For collection of *Hydra*, they can be found in shallow water of ponds, lakes and streams and can be easily collected in early winter months. The acquatic vegetation containing these animals may be put in a jar full of pond water. To separate them from the twig, a jet of water from pipette will separate them. When they are ex- tended, they may be fixed in Bouin's fluid and stored in 70% alcohol.

MORPHOLOGY

Size

Hydra is easily visible to the naked eye. Its size, ranges from 2 to 20 mm. in length. The great variation in length is due to the remarkable power of contraction and expansion possessed by it.

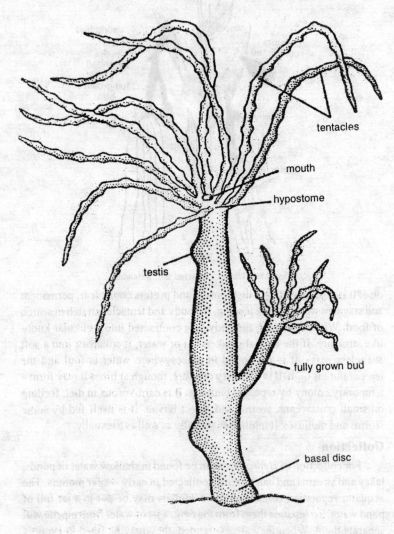

Fig. 2.2. *Hydra*.

Colour

Colour varies from species to species. *Hydra vulgaris* is almost colourless, *Hydra oligactis* is brown, while *Chlorohydra viridissima* is green. The green colour of the last named species is due to the presence of a unicellular green alga (*Chlorella vulgaris*) in the cells lining the digestive cavity. Colour of *Hydra* often depends on the nature of food and hence cannot be used in identification of species with certainty.

Form

The body of *Hydra* has the form of a tube. Its proximal end is closed by flat disc termed the *basal disc* or foot. The latter fixes the body to the substratum by a sticky secretion and also helps in locomotion. It has in some species a pore which remains closed during attachment. The distal free end of the body has a small conical projection, the *hypostome* or *oral cone*, perforated at the apex by a circular aperture, the *mouth*. A ring of 4-12 fine hollow processes, the *tentacles*, surrounds the base of the hypostome. The number of tentacles differs between species and increases with the age of the animal. The size of the tentacles also varies with the

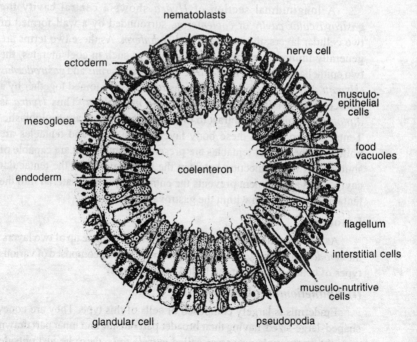

Fig. 2.3. T.S. of *Hydra*.

species. They are shorter than the body in *Chlorohydra viridissima,* slightly longer than the body in *Hydra vulgaris* and much longer than the body in *Hydra oligactis.* The tentacles are highly extensible and may stretch out from short blunt projections to extremely thin threads 7 cm. or more long and hardly visible even with a lens. They are primarily meant for catching food, but are also used for locomotion. They are between the basal disc and the hypostome in the body proper or column.

Often one to several buds are found in the column region, and these in turn may bear buds before detachment from the parent. In this way a sort of primitive *Hydra* colony is formed. In *H. oligactis*, there is a definite *budding zone.* Others less conspicuous structures that may be occasstionally seen on the external surface of the column includes reproductive organs i.e. testes and ovaries. *Testes* are papillated conical elevations, situated near the hypostome while the *ovaries* are knob-like, usually located near the basal end. Reproductive organs are particularly prominent in the autumn and winter

HISTOLOGY

A longitudinal section of *Hydra* shows a central cavity the *gastrovascular cavity* or *coelenteron,* surrounded by a wall formed of two cellular layers, the *ectoderm* and *endoderm.* As these two terms are generally limited to embryological stages, as such in coelenterates, the two epithelia are now preferred to be called as *epidermis* and *gastrodermis* (*Hyman*, 1940).The epidermis and gastrodermis are joined together by a non-cellular gelatinous layer, called the *mesogloea.* Thus *Hydra* is *diploblastic* animal in contrast to higher animals which are triploblastic. Tentacles also posses these body layers. Both body and tentacles are hollow; at the base of tentacles are present sphincters that are capable of shutting off the connection between the body cavity and the tentacular cavity. This arratgement prevents the entry of injurious material into the tentacular cavity ftom within the gastrovascular cavity.

Ectoderm

As already stated that *Hydra* is diploblastic i.e. made up of two layers: the *ectoderm* and, the *gasterderm.* Ectoderm is further composed of various types of cells given under the following sub-heads:

(i) Epitheliomuscular cells

Epidermis is largely composed of cells of this type. They are cone-shaped, large-sized, having their broader part outside and inner part drawn out into contractible processes called *muscle tails,* these lie just outside the mesogloea and resting over it. The broader part of a cell press against

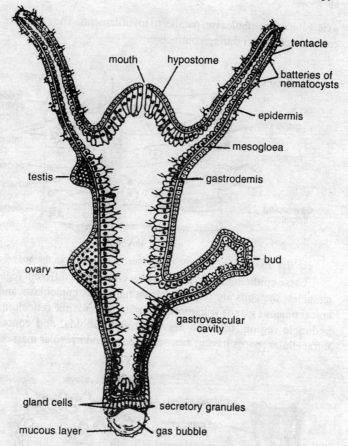

Fig. 2.4. *Hydra*. Longitudinal section of the body and tentacles.

those of neighbouring cells, thus epidermal cells form a continuous layer over the body surface, while the narrow inner parts leave narrow spaces between them. The outer border bears fine membrane-bound mucous granules that secrete a thick filamentous protective material outside. The cytoplasm of the cell has smooth and rough endoplasmic reticulum, free ribosomes, Golgi complex, number of mitochondria and quite a few intracellular space. and vacuoles. The adjacent cells are connected by septate desmosomes. Muscle-tails have longitudinally running contractile fibres, the *myofilaments,* that branch and anastomose, and one or more non-contractible supporting fibrils called *tonofibrils.* Longitudinal arrangement of muscle-tails allows contraction of the body along the long axis. Fine microtubules run parallel to myofilaments. They are believed to carry ions or water during contraction.

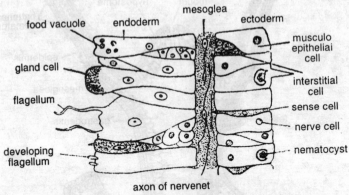

Fig. 2.5. *Hydra*. Diagrammatic longitudinal section through the body-wall.

These epitheliomuscular cells show variation in different regions. In tentacles, the cells are large and have numerous cnidoblasts and more apical mucous glands with more elaborate endoplasmic reticulum. In the peduncle region, the cells are small and cuboidal and contain few intracellular spaces having mucous granules and irregular masses.

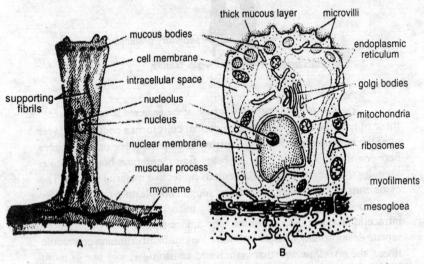

Fig. 2.6. *Hydra*. An epithelio-muscular cell. A Under light microscope. B Under electron microscope

(ii) Glandulomuscular cells

The epitheliomuscular cells of the pedal disc are specialised to secret adhesive material to provide attachment to the substratum. The interior of these cells is filled witl mucous granules which are elaborated by Golgi complex. The endoplasinic reticulum is well developed. The basal region of the cells have smaller mucous granules while the apex has larger ones.

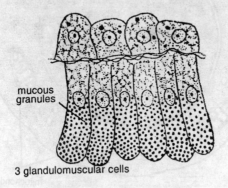

mucous
granules

3 glandulomuscular cells

Fig. 2.7. Cells of *Hydra*.

(iii) Interstitial cells

In between the narrow ends of epitheliomuscular cells, there are empty spaces (interstice) which are filled with small cells called *interstitial* or *formative* or *packing cells*. They are looked upon as embryonic cells, reminiscent of the archaeocytes of Porifera, and are capable of giving rise to other cells of epidermis as well as forming nematocysts. At certain periods of the year some develop into reproductive cell. Thus interstitial cells play an important role in regeneration, growth, budding and sexual reproduction.

(iv) Sensory cells

These are tall, narrow cells scattered amongst the epitheliomuscular cells and project over the surface by the single *sensory cilium* with rooting fibres lying in the cytoplasm. At the apical surface of the cell, which reaches the surface of the body, the plasma membrane is notched to form a collar for the cilium. The modified cilium consists of nine peripheral and more than two central fibrils. Their inner ends are drawn out not into muscle-tails but into thin *modulated fibres*. Small rooting fibres radiate out from the basal granule of the cilium. Mitochondria, endoplasmic vesicles and microtubules are present.

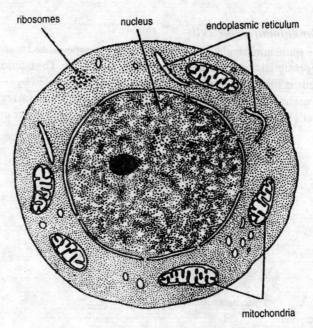

ribosomes   nucleus   endoplasmic reticulum

mitochondria

Fig. 2.8. *Hydra.* Diagrammatic representation of an electron micrograph of an interstitial cell.

The detailed study with the help of electron microscope shows that a single cilium-like process, the apical cilium, with 9+2 fibrillar pattern occurs in the apex of cell which is surrounded by a cell membrane. The basal end of the sensory cell either rests on the nerve cell or is connected to its process.

(v) Nerve cells

The nerve cells or ganglion cells are small and elongated having one or more processes. They are situated at the base of the epitheliomuscular cells just above their muscular process. They are derived from the interstitial cells of epidermis. Each nerve cell consists of a small cell body with a nucleus and gives off two to several nerve pocesses or nuritis. The nuritis of adjacent nerve cells do not fuse but only touch each other. The nerve cells of the whole body are linked up by synaptic contacts to form a sort of nerve net. The nucleus, endoplasmic reticulum, scattered mitochondria, two or three groups of Golgi complex, many small and large fluid filled vesicles and microtubles, which extend into nerve processes or nurities. The latter contain ribosome, mitochondria, fluid-filled sacs amd microtubules. The nerve cells of the basal part are devoid of microtubules.

(vi) Germ cells

During summer, the interstitial cells in certain restricted regions of the body repeatedly divide and proliferate reproductive cells forming gonads, which later differentiate into either *testes* or *ovaries*.

(vii) Cnidoblasts

Cnidoblasts or stinging cells are found scattered throughout the epidermis but are more abundant on the tentacles. These are developed by some of the interstitial cells which get specialised. When fully formed, they migrate towards the tentacles through the mesogloea by means of amoeboid movement. The cnidoblast cells are somewhat oval-shaped.

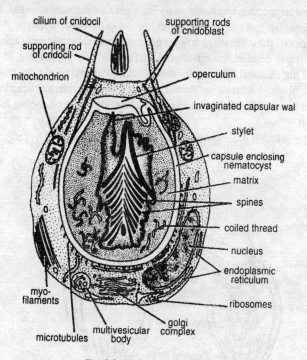

Fig. 2.9. *Hydra*. A cnidoblast

The cnidoblast possesses a thin cytoplasmic rim which surrounds the large centrally located nematocyst. The nucleus is situated between the nematocyst and plasma membrane and contains a small inconspicuous nucleolus. A few rough surfaced lamellae and isolated smooth surfaced vesicles of endoplasmic reticulum are present in the cytoplasm. Free ribosomes are also present. Small Golgi complex lies in the basal region.

Mitochondira, lipid droplets and multivesicular bodies are located in the cytoplasm. Extending from the capsule of the nematocyst are a bundle of small myofilaments. A peculiar oval or pyriform sac or bladder filled with a poisonous fluid or *hypnotoxin*, which is a chemical mixture of proteins and phenols, is present. This is the *stinging cell* or *nematocyst*.

Nematocysts (Gr., *nema*, thread + *kysics*, bladder) is a minute sac, 5 to 50 μ in length. It is not a cell because it is chitinous and non-living. The outer end of nematocyst is invaginated into a long, hollow and tubular thread coiled like a wire-spring inside the sac. The tip of the thread tube is open and its base is swollen to form the shaft. The inturned thread is covered over at the base by an operculum. At the base of the thread tube are three large spine-like *barbs* or *stylets* which are directed inwards. There are three spiral rows of minute spines known as *barbules* or *spines*. A hair-like process, the *cnidocil* or trigger projects from the outer end of the cell and extends beyond the epidermal surface. A few supporting rods lie around the cnidocil. The cytoplasm of cnidoblast may have contractible muscle fibres. A restraining thread, the *lasso* is sometimes attached to the base of nematoblast which prevents the nematocyst from being thrown out of it.

The cnidocil is composed of a central core surrounded by large rods.

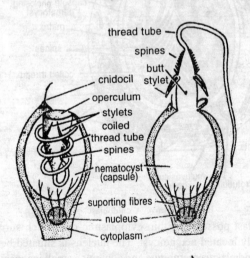

Fig. 2.10. *Hydra.* A cnidoblast. A—Undischarged. B—Discharged.

Origin and occurrence of nematocysts

The nematocysts have their origin in the vacuoles of the interstitial cells. The cnidoblasts containing developing nematocysts migrate through the body wall into the coelenteron from where they are taken up by pseudopodia of endodermal cells and transferred to mesogloa through which they travel and migrate outwards through the body wall again and reach the final position to complete the development. The cnidoblasts get fixed in the ectoderm with its base reaching the mesogloea while the cnidocil bores through the cutcile and projects outside. The nematocysts are scattered individually throughout the epidermis of the body except the basal disc where they are absent. They occur abundantly in the oral region and in the tentacles, as wart-like "nematycyst batteries", each battery consisting of one or two large central nematocysts surrounded by 10-12 smaller nematocysts. All of them are enclosed in a single larger epithelio-muscle cell. However, they are never formed in the tentacles but migrate from their place of origin in the epidermis of body.

The nematocysts are weapons of offense and defence of *Hydra*. They also serve in food capture, locomotion and anchorage.

Discharging of Nematocyst

The process of the discharge of nematocyst is quite peculiar. Whenever the cnidocil comes in contact with any object such as protozoans, then a kind of stimulus passes through the cytoplasm of the nematoblast due to which the contractile fibrils surrounding the capsule contract. By the contraction of these fibrils pressure is exerted on the capsule due to which the operculum opens.

The pressure in the fluid of the capsule is increased so much that the whole funnel and the thread tube coiled around it immediately shoots out of the capsule. The thread of capsule penetrates the body of the animal. A poisonous substance comes out of the thread tube and enters the body of the animal, which becomes unconscious. Once discharged, the nematocyst becomes useless and drops off from the body of *Hydra*. A new nematoblast migrates to its place.

Mechanism of discharge of nematocyst

The mechanism of the discharge of the nematocyst is not yet fully understood. There are many views regarding it.

1. According to the old view, the nematocyst discharged because of the increase in pressure on the fluid of the capsule.
2. According to *Iwanzoff* and *Vanagita* and others, some amount of the cytoplasm of the nematoblast diffuses into the capsule and increases the pressure of its fluid due to which the nematocyst discharges.

3. According to *Jones* (1947), the nematocysts is always in a state of tension and with stimulation of the cnidocil, the operculum opens and due to its own force of tension the nematocyst discharges automatically.

4. Recent researches have shown the presence of a substance called adenosine triphosphate (A.T.P.) inside and outside the nematocyst which indicate that probably this substance plays important in the mechanism of the discharge of nematocyst.

KINDS OF NEMATOCYSTS

Nematocysts are of four kinds :

1. Penetrant or Stenotele.
2. Volvent or Desmonemes.
3. Streptoline glutinant or Holotrichous isorhizas.
4. Stereoline glutinant or Atrichous isorhizas.

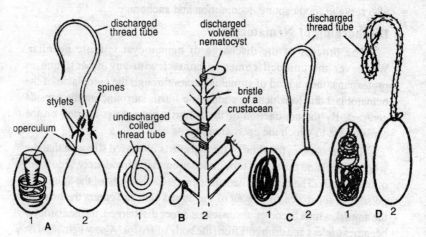

Fig. 2.11. *Hydra*. Kinds of nematocysts. A–Penetrant. B–Volvent. C–Steroline glutinant. D–Stereoline glutinant. D–Streptoline glutinant. 1–Undischarged.   2–Discharged.

Penetrant

This kind of nematocyst is large and spherical. It is about 16μ in diameter. It occupies the entire cnidoblast, in which it lies. Before being discharged, it is pear-shaped. The thread-tube, which is situated inside it is coiled transversely. At its base are found three large and three small rows of spines or thorns. When discharged, it pierces the body of the prey and injects the *hypnotoxin* by which the prey is paralysed.

Volvent

This kind of nematocyst is relatively small and pearshaped (9μ long). It has in it a short thread-tube, which is coiled in a single loop, when the nematocyst is discharged its short thread-tube coil around the hairs of the prey.

Streptoline glutinant

This type of nematocyst is large, cylindrical and pointed at the ends, where thread is discharged (9μ). The thread-tube is longer than that of the volvent and is rolled in three or four transverse coils. It posses a spiral row of minute thorns and it twists and coils upon discharging.

Stereoline glutinant

This type of nematocyst is the smallest (7μ). Its shape is oval and it possesses thread-tube, which is discharged straight, and is without any barbs or thorns.

The nematocysts are most common on tentacles where all the four types are present while hypostome has only large glutinant type of nematocysts. The rest of the body has only large glutinant and stereoline types of nematocysts. The discharge of nematoeysts is not under the control of the nervous system but they are independent effectors. Even nematocysts removed from the body of *Hydra* will shoot out their thread if an adequate stimulus is applied.

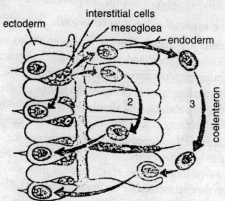

Fig. 2.12. *Hydra.* Migration of nematoblast.

An epitheliomuscular cell of a tentacle contains a group of nematocysts, each in its own cnidoblast. Such a group of nematocysts is called a *battery*. There may be as many as 12 nematocysts in a battery and these include 1 or 2 stenoteles surrounded by desmonemes and isorhizas.

The cluster of various cnidocytes possessed by a cnidarian are referred to as the *cnidom* and are very useful in classifying the species. A total of eighteen types of nematocysts have been described. The distinctions amongst them is mainly in the character of their tubular thread; in one type the tube is closed at the tip, in the other, it is open. Nematocysts with closed threads are called *astomocnidae,* others with open threads are called *stomocnidae.*

Mesogloea

Mesogloea or mesolamella is a non-cellular, thin layer lying between the epidermis and gastrodermis. It is attached to both the layers. It is secreted by gastrodermis and extends in the entire body and tentacles being thickest in the stalk and thinnest in the tentacles so that the pedal region is able to withstand great mechanical strain and provide flexibility to tentacles. The mesogloea gives rigidity and support to the body and acts as a sort of elastic skeleton.

Gastrodermis

The gastrodermis is the inner layer of the body wall which surrounds the bag-like gastrovascular cavity. It forms about two third of the entire thickness of the body wall. Its structure is almost similar to that of epidermis and is formed of large, often vacuolated and flagellated or amoeboid columnar cells. It is mainly secretory, digestive, muscular and sensory in nature. The following types of cells are present.

(i) Nutritive muscular or digestive cells

These cells are almost similar to the epithelio-muscular cells of epidermis. They are long and club-shaped, their outer ends have two process containing myonemes which do not branch. The myonemes lie at right angles to the long axis of the body and form a circular muscle layer by which the animal contracts and slowly expends the body. A few of these cells serve as sphincters to close the mouth and cavities of tentacles. These cells are best developed in the hypostome and the bases of tentacles. They are highly vacuolated and contain food vacuoles, the free ends usually bear two flagella. The nutritive cells may also secrete digestive enzymes into the coelenteron for the digestion of food. The whip-lik flagella keep the liquid food inside the body cavity in motion. The cells may also give out blunt pseudopodia to engulf food particles.

The ultrastructure of the cells shows that the free end is produced into microvilli and two or more flagella. The latter extend into the gastrovascular cavity and contain 9+2 pattern of fibres. The cytoplasm includes a large number of mitochondria, glycogen granules, secretory granules and food vacuoles. The endoplasmic reticulum and free ribosomes are present in abundance. Centrally placed-nucleus has one nucleolus. The small Golgi complex lies close to the nucleus. The ultrastructure of digestive cells suggests that the cells of stomach, and hypostome serve for ingestion and digestion.

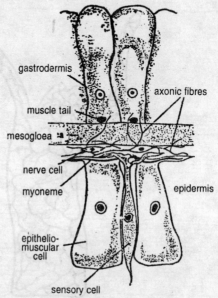

gastrodermis
axonic fibres
muscle tail
mesogloea
nerve cell
myoneme
epidermis
epithelio-muscular cell
sensory cell

Fig. 2.13. *Hydra*. Neuro-sensory system.

(ii) Endothelio-gland cells

The endothelio-gland cells are smaller than nutritive-muscular cells and occur interspread among them. They lack muscle tails at tapering basal ends but bear one or two flagells at their free ends. The endothelio-gland cells are of two types. The *enzymatic gland cells* secrete digestive enzymes, which are poued into the enteron for extracellular digestion. In the region of hypostome and mouth are found *mucous glands cells,* which secrete a slimy fluid serving as a lubricant and also for entangling and paralysing the prey. Gland cells are absent in the tentacles and the pedal disc. They are independent effectors as they are not controlled by the nervous system. They are believed to develop from interstitial cells.

(iii) Interstitial cells

A few interstitial cells occur between the endothelio-nutritive-muscle cells. These are *totipotent* as they give rise to gland cells, sensory cells, reproductive cells and nerve cells.

(iv) Sensory cells

The sensory cells are also found in the gastrodermis. They are supposed to be stimulated by the entry of the prey into the gastrovascular cavity.

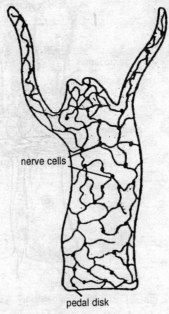

Fig. 2.14. *Hydra.* Nerve-net.

(v) Nerve-cells

There is a net-work of nerve-cells with long processes found in the ectoderm or epidermis in close contact with mesogloea they also form the network in the endoderm. Each nerve-cell consists of a cell having a nucleus. The body of the cell is elongated in the form of fibres, which anastomoses to form a network known as nerve-net. Some nerve-fibres are connected with musculo-epithelial cells, while others are in relation with receptor cells.

By the type of arrangement of nerve-net, strong stimulus is carried to every part of the body. If tentacles are stimulated, not only the tentacles but also the whole body contracts. This system, although resembles with the telephone system, yet is not an efficient one.

Nutrition

Food. Hydra is a carnivorous animal; it eats large quantities greedily. Its food is cyclops, small crustaceans, insect-larvae, annelids etc. Some large specimens of *Hydra* also engulf young fishes and tadpoles, and can take even pieces of meat artificially. *Jennings* recorded a case in which *Hydra* engulfed a catterpillar, which was approximately fifty times the size of the *Hydra*. Usually, *Hydra* captures food of smaller size.

Sometimes, when *Hydra* is very hungry, it dips into the water and fills the gastrovascular cavity with the ooze.

Ingestion

Coelenterates are the first animals to use projectiles, called *nematocysts*, for capturing animals. The volvents coil around bristles and other appendages on the prey, while the glutinants fasten to its surface, thus holding it fast. The penetrants puncture the victim and inject the paralysing fluid or *hypnotoxin*. Other tentacles may also perform coordinated movements and shoot prey their batteries of nematocysts. The tentacles, holding the prey, now contract and bend inward drawing the paralysed prey towards the mucous-lined mouth, which opens widely to swallow it. Mucous secretions help in swallowing and the mouth can be greatly distended. Contractions of the hypostome and body wall (peristaltic movements) force the food down into the gastrovascular cavity where digestion takes place.

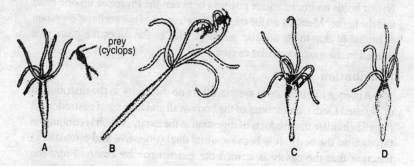

prey
(cyclops)

A   B   C   D

Fig. 2.15. *Hydra.* Capturing and ingesting a *Cyclops.*

The food varies greatly accoding to the state of the animal. A very well-fed *Hydra* will not react to food when it is pesented, while a hungry *Hydra* will repsond even when a chemical stimulus, such as beef juice, is added to the water. A chemical, called *glutathione,* usually found in tissue fluids of most animals, is necessary to evoke feeding reaction. Thus, *Hydra* engulf only those animals which have glutathione in their body.

Digestion

The digestion of the prey occurs in two stages. First, the prey is killed by the action of the digestive juice secreted by the gland cells of the gastrodermis. The churning movements caused by the expansion and contraction of the body wall and the lashing movements of flagella of the nutritive muscle cells thoroughly mix up the digestive juice with the food which is broken into smaller particles suspended in a meaty broth. The digestive enzymes react upon the disintegrating food. The proteolytic enzyme similar to trypsin partly digests the proteins into polypeptides. The tissue of the prey turns into a soupy broth. This type of digestion, occurring in the cavity, outside the gastrodermal cells is called *extracellular digestion*. It also takes place in the stomach and intestine of most multicellular animals like frog, earthworm, etc. It is met with in *Hydra* for the first time.

Smaller fragments of food are then engulfed by the nutritive muscle cells by means of pseudopodia and digested within food vacuoles, where *intracellular digestion* occurs, as in Protozoa and Porifera, but unknown in the vertebrates. Within food vacuoles the further digestion of proteins and fats takes place. Studies have revealed that the food vacuoles undergo both acidic as well as alkaline phases, Digestion in *Hydra,* therefore, is quite interesting, since it combines the digestive procedures of forms both lower (Protozoa) and higher (Vertebrates) than itself. In this respect, *Hydra* holds an intermediate position between the Protozoa on one hand and the higher Metazoa on the other. The retention of intracellular digestion is probably due to its aquatic mode of life, as the digestive juice gets diluted in the gastrovascular cavity.

Distribution

Absence of circulatory system offers no difficulty in the distribution of digested food. Contractions of the body-wall and lashing of gastrodermal flagella circulate the products of digestion in the cavity, which is continuous throughout the body. It is because of its dual (digestive and circulatory) function that the cavity is termed the *gastrovascular cavity*. From the cavity, the digested food is absorbed into the gastrodermal cells. From here, some of it diffuses through the mesogloca into the epidermal cells. Certain gastrodermal cells, after capturing the food-particles, break off from their neighbouring cells and either move in an amoeboid manner or are carried passively by currents set up by the flagella into the tentacles where they are ingested. Even fragments of gastrodermal cells also distribute the food in a similar way.

Assimilation

The food absorbed into the cells is transformed into protoplasm. A part of the food, especially the oil globules, is stored in the epidermal cells for use in the production of energy.

Egestion

The indigestible residues are cast off by gastrodermal cells into the enteron. From here, they are expelled out through the mouth by a series of violent contractions of the body-wall. The debris falls some distance away from the animal.

Locomotion

Hydra is mostly attached by the basal disc to some suitable object in the water. While stationary, the body and tentacles twist and move in various directions to capture food. But they also show actual movement from one place to another. They perform movement either in response to light or some chemical stimulus or in search of food. The contraction and expansion of the contractile muscle fibres of epidermis bring about locomotion. The following types of movements are found in *Hydra:*

(i) Expansion and contraction

Hydra, when hungry, remains attached to a substratum in water and frequently expands and contracts itself at intervals. This movement is performed to bring food particles in contact with the tentacles which are waved all around in water. Also, contraction of one side and elongation of other side of the body or tentacles result in the bending and swaying movements which assist in the capture of prey.

Fig. 2.16. *Hydra* showing somersaulting movement.

(ii) Somersaulting

This type of locomotion resembles the looping type of locomotion. The body bends in the direction in which it has to move in the same manner as in looping locomotion. The tentacles take a firm hold of the substratum and the basal disc is released. The body now straightens up in such a manner that the animal stand up side down, i.e. the oral end with its tentacles holding the substratum and the released basal disc pointing upwards. The body now bends once again in the forward direction so that the basal disc touches and then becomes fixed up to the substratum ahead of the oral end. The tentacles release their hold on the substratum and the animal regains its erect position, i.e. basal disc, attached to the substratum and oral end with its tentacles pointing upwards.

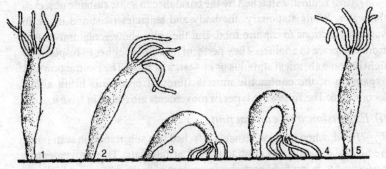

Fig. 2.17. *Hydra* showing looping movements.

(iii) Looping

Hydra can also move from place to place in search of food. Usually the body first extends and then bends over, so that the tentacles attach to the substratum with the help of adhesive glutinant nematocysts. Then the

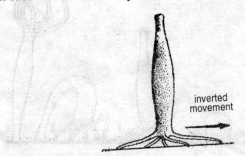

inverted
movement

Fig. 2.18. *Hydra* showing cuttle-fish like movements.

pedal disc is released and brought up closer to the circlet of tentacles and attached. The tentacles now loosen their hold and the body becomes erect again. The whole process which is repeated again and again appears like a series of looping movements of a caterpillar or leech.

(iv) Gliding

Provides only small and slow movement along its attachment by alternate contraction and expansion of basal disc. It is brought about by creeping amoeboid movement of the cells of the pedal disc which gives out pseudopodia like projections. The animal can, sometimes, creeps considerable distance by this method.

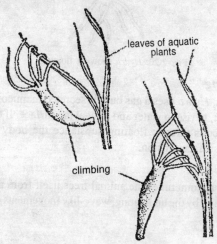

leaves of aquatic plants

climbing

Fig. 2.19. *Hydra* showing climbing.

(v) Walking

Occasionally, *Hydra* becomes inverted and stands on its tentacles and moves in an inverted condition, using its tentacles as if they were legs. This type of movement takes, place on some object such as leaf and in leisurely hours.

(vi) Climbing

While changing location in a limited area, *Pelmatohydra oligactis*, can even clim by attaching its long tentacles to some object, releasing the foot, and then contracting the tentacles, so that the body is lifted up the object.

(vii) Floating

Very often *Hydra* exhibits the floating movements. The cells at the basal disc release large bubble of gas in mucous which helps the animals to float and rises to water surface.

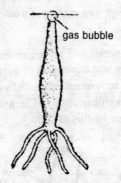

gas bubble

Fig. 2.20. *Hydra* showing floating.

(viii) Surfacing

Sometimes, *Hydra* uses a gas bubble secreted in mucous by the cells of the pedal disc, to rise in water and float at the surface. If the gas bubble bursts, the mocous threads floating substance the body on the water surface due to surface tension.

(ix) Swimming

It is said that sometimes the animal frees itself from the substratum and swims in water by the undulating, wave-like movements of the tentacles and the body.

Growth

Growth in *Hydra* involves the division of all types of cells except the cnidoblasts. The latter are formed from the interstitial cells. The growth chiefly takes place just below the bases of the tentacles. From this growing region, new cells are added either towards the tentacles or towards the basal disc. Old cells are constantly sloughed off from the basal disc and tips of the tentacles to be replaced by new ones pushed down from the growing region. Under normal conditions this process continue indefinitey. For this, *Brien* and other consider *Hydr* to be immortal.

Respiration and the excretion

There are no special respiratory and excretory organs in *Hydra*. Respiration and excretion are only possible by the general surface of the body. Oxygen diffuses into the cells from water and carbon dioxide passes out of the cells. Nitrogenous waste products are also removed by the general surface of the body.

Behaviour

Reaction to the stimuli in *Hydra* is affected by contact, reaction to the chemicals, reaction to temperature-changes and reaction to light.

(a) Thigmotropism (reaction to contact)

By non-localized stimulus i.e., the one which affects the animal as a whole, *Hydra* responds by withdrawing tentacles and by contraction of the body. But if there is a localized stimulation, the response to the stimuli will be in the area affected, which may cause withdrawal of a single tentacle or bending of the whole body.

(b) Chemotropism (reaction to chemicals)

The response to chemicals is due to the nature of the chemicals. The *Hydra* avoids injurious chemicals. It responds positively to the presence of food. In food taking reaction, both chemotropism and thigmotropism are involved.

(c) Phototropism (reaction to light)

Hydra moves towards optimum light by the *trial and error method.* Green *Hydra* moves towards intense light.

(d) Thermotropism (reaction to temperature)

Hydra become active in the water, kept at a temperature approximately 31ºC. They flourish in cool water. *Hydra* are also found in abundance under ice in winter but do not survive in a temperature raised in a shallow pool by exposure to summer sun.

(e) Periodic contraction-bursts

This is a characteristics feature of the behaviour pattern, by which the animal contracts so as to form a tight ball. The contractions are followed by extensions, which take place every five to ten minutes in day-light. However, the frequency becomes much less at night *McCullogh* (1963) pointed out that these bursts serve for regular intermittent sampling of the environment around the *Hydra*.

REPRODUCTION

Hydra reproduces asexually as well asexually. Asexual reproduction is more common than the sexual reproduction, secondly asexual reproduction takes place during favourable condition whereas sexual reproduction takes place during unfavourable circumstances.

1. Asexual reproduction

It takes place in the following three ways:

  (a) Budding
  (b) Grafting
  (c) Fission

(a) Budding

Hydra reproduces by this method under favourable conditions i.e. when food is available to it in plenty and the temperature of the water is also suitable. During this process, the nutritive substances start accumulating in the ectodermal cells of its body. Small projections appear in its body by repeated divisions of the ectodermal cells in these regions. These pojections are called *buds*. Ectoderm and endoderm both take part in their fomation. These are hollow and connected with the gastrovascular cavity. These gradually grow and in the end become narrow tube-like. Their internal and external structures both are like the parent *Hydra*. The tentacles are present at their free ends. The mouth is surrounded by these tentacles. The bud starts constricting at the place where it is attached to the parent body and gradually separates from the parent to become a young *Hydra* which performs all its life activities independently. Sometimes, these buds do not separate from the parent and remain attached to it. Thus they give rise to a branched *Hydra*. If the favourable conditions continue to exist then *Hydra* goes on increasing its species by this method of budding.

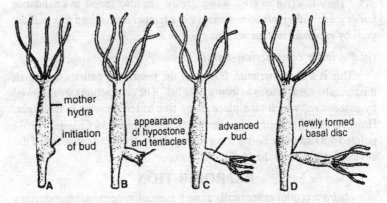

Fig. 2.21. *Hydra*. Budding.

(b) Grafting

The grafting in *Hydra* has been in the same way as it is done in plants. This method has been successfully used in *Chlorohydra viridissima*. Two such hydras are taken. One of these is kept in dark so that its chlorophyll decomposes and it becomes white in colour. Now this white and the other green *Hydra* are both cut transversely through the middle by a sharp knife. The lower half of the white *Hydra* is attached to the upper half of the green *Hydra* and the remaining two halves are also attached to each other. After some time, the white and green halves fuse to form a *Hydra* which reproduces by *budding*. The buds which arise at the junction have their upper part green and lower part white.

(c) Fission

Sometimes, the body of *Hydra* constricts transversely or longitudinally into two parts. Each part forms the necessary organs and develops into a complete *Hydra*.

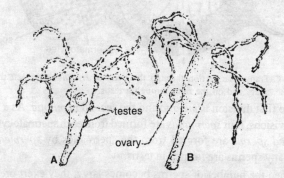

Fig. 2.22. *Hydra.* Male and Female.

2. Sexual Reproduction

In *Hydra*, the sexual reproduction takes place under unfavourable conditions. Whenever there is lack of food and oxygen or the temperature becomes much high or low then the reproductive organs start forming in *Hydra*. These animals are bisexual and the development of reproductive organs takes place from the interstitial cells.The reproductive organs are different from buds chiefly in two respects. (1) ectoderm and endodenn both are present in buds but endoderm is absent in reproductive organs (2) the vary buds are hollow with an internal cavity but the reproductive organs are solid. In *Hydra*, the reproductive organs are formed only during the breeding season and they disappear after it.Their breeding season extends from the end of rainy season to the beginning of the winter.

Testes

They are formed in the upper part of the body and are cone-shaped. The *interstitial cells* of the testis divide repeatedly to form *sperm mother cells* or *spermatogonia*. Each *sperm mother cells* divides twice and changes into *primary spermatocytes*. The spermatogenesis now takes place in each spermatocyte during which it divides by two maturation divisions.

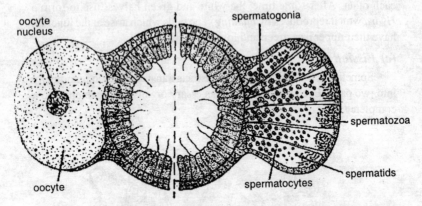

Fig. 2.23. Transverse section through the body of *Hydra*–on the left through an ovary and on the right through a testis.

The first division is *meiotic* and the second in *mitotic*. As a result of these divisions, four *spermatids* are formed from each spermatocyte. Later, the *tailed sperms* are formed from the spermatids by *spermeogenesis*. Thus many sperms are formed in testis.

When the number of sperms becomes large, they exert pressure on the wall of the testis, which ruptures at its knob-like part called nipple and the sperms are released in the water where they swim freely with the help of their tails.

Ovaries

They are formed in the lower part of the body of *Hydra*. There are many *interstitial cells* in each ovary multiply to form oogonia. One of these cells, called oocyte, becomes larger and amoeboid with a big nucleus is seen. After some time, two divisions take place in this cell. The first division is meiotic and the second is mitotic. Thus in each ovary, an ovum and two *polar bodies* are formed. When the ectoderm over the ovum ruptures by contraction, it forms a cup-like cushion around the ovum which becomes implant at that place in a protruding condition. This *Hydra* state is known as protendrous condition. This is the reason why cross fertilization does not occur in *Hydra*. The fully matured ovum must be fertilized within 24 hours on its becoming exposed in the water otherwise it would become useless and dies.

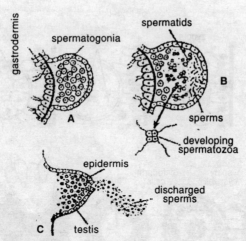

Fig. 2.24. A–B–Ripening of a testis in *H.oligactis*, C–in *H. littoralis*.

At the time of fertilization the ovum attracts the sperms or spermatozoa towards itself. Only one sperm penetrates the ovum. The head alone of the penetratings sperm enters the ovum and the tail is left outside. After this the nueleus of the sperm fuses with the nucleus of the ovum and a diploid *zygote* or *oospore* is formed.

Cleavage and development

Zygote, still stated in the epidermal cup cover its mother, undergoes segmentation or cleavage. Within a short time, zygote is transformed into a hollow *blastula* or *coeloblastula*, cells of which, the *blastomeres,* are all equal in size and surround a fluid-filled,cavity, the *blastocoel.* Later, as *blastomeres* multipiy by quick divisions, some cells leave the surface and migrate by *primary delamination* into the interior from all directions (*multipolar ingression*), and obliterate the blastocoel. The embryo is now known as a *gastrula.* A new cavity or space develops in the gastrula, this is surrounded by the cells that migrated into the interior and is called archenteron. So the gastrula has two layers of cells, an outer, the *ectoderm,* and an inner, the *endoderm.* Meanwhile, ectodermal cells have been secreting a chitinoid spiny *cyst* or *theca* around the embryo. The encysted embryo is detached from the parent body and falls to the bottom. Ponds may dry up and cysts blown off by the wind or carried by water-birds on their feet and breaks from one pond to the other.

Hatching

The encysted embryo remains dormant and unchanged for several weeks, until the next spring. As it can withstand drying and freezing, it

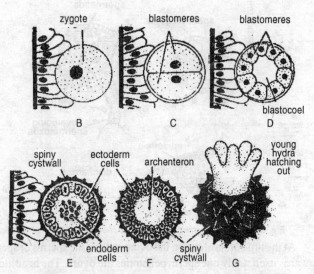

Fig. 2.25.   *Hydra*. Fertilization and stages of development. A–Fertilization of an
ovum. B–Zygote. C–Cleavage. D–Blastula. E–Early gastrula and
encystation. F–Gastrula. G–Young *Hydra* hatching.

carries the race through droughts and winters. It is also probable that this
resting stage serves for dispersal, for it can be carried by currents of wind,
or in mud on the feet of animals to other ponds in which water is present.

With the advent of favourable conditions of water and temperature
development is resumed. *Interstitial cells* arise in the ectoderm and
mesogloea is secreted between the two cellular layers. The embryo
elongated, and a circlet of tentacle buds develop at one end with a mouth
appearing to their midst. As the embryo increases in size, the outer cyst
wall softens to break open and the embryo hatches into a partially
differentiated polyp. There is no free larval stage in the development of
Hydra. This life-history of *Hydra*, thus, has the scheme: polyp—egg—
polyp.

REGENERATION

Regeneration is the ability of an organism to replace its damage body
parts. It usually occurs whenever the body is injured or can also be induced
artificially by mutilation, the power to regenerate was first reported in 1744
in *Hydra*, by its discoverer *Abraham Trembly*. Regenerative power also
occur in many other coelenterates and other invertebrates, but *Hydra*
alone has been a favourite material for experimentations.

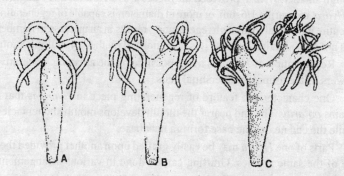

Fig. 2.26. *Hydra* showing the formation of multiheaded specimen by regeneration, A–Single heade *Hydra*, B–Two headed *Hydra*, C–Four headed *Hydra*.

A. *Trembly* (1744) found that if a living *Hydra* is cut across into two, three or more pieces, each grows the missing parts and becomes a complete

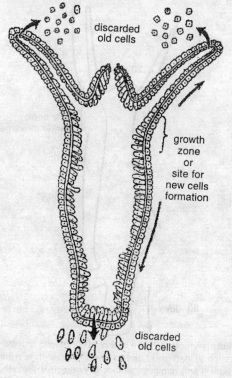

Fig. 2.27. Cell replacement in *Hydra*.

though smaller, *Hydra,* provided the pieces are not too small. A fragment of *Hydra*, measuring 1/6 mm. or more in diameter, is capable of regenerating an entire individual. Although regenerating results in an increase in number, it is not reproduction because it is not a normal method of multiplicaion.

Regeneration of *Hydra* is made possible by the amazing. generative powers of the totipotent interstitial cells.

One characteristic feature of regenerating piece in *Hydra* is that it retains *polarity.* The end nearer the mouth develops mouth and tentacles, while the end nearer the base forms a new base.

Parts of one *Hydra* may be easily grafted upon another provided they are of the same species. Grafting can be done in various arrangements producing many bizarre effects.

A. Trembly observed if the head end of a *Hydra* is split in two and the parts are separated slightly, it results into a Y-shaped specimen, or "two-headed" individual, having two mouths and two sets of tentacles. Each

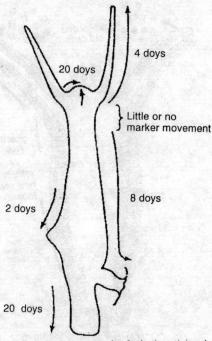

Fig. 2.28.   Tissue movement in *Hydra* as a result of mitotic activity. Arrows indicate direction of movement and numbers indicate days required for cells to movement and numbers indicate days required for cells to move along path of arrow.

head may be again split in a similar manner. Thus, *Trembly* succeeded in producing a "seven- headed" *Hydra*. It was the great regenerative power of these animals which won for them the name "*Hydra*", after a Greek mythological monster which was finally destroyed by *Herculeus*. According to the legend, '*Hydra*' had nine heads and sooner did *Herculeus* cut one off, than two grew in its place.

IMMORTALITY IN *HYDRA*

The immortality of *Hydra* has been described by *P. Brien* 1955. According to him there is a *growth* just below the tentacles where interstitial cells give rise to all other cells of the body. With the formation of new cells, old cells are pushed towards the end of the tentacles and the pedal disc, from where they are shed to outside. In about 45 days, the older body cells are replaced by new cells. This process of cell replacement is an endless process. It has also been shown that, if the interstitial cells of the growth zone are destroyed , the *Hydra* lives only few days.

Revision Questions

1. Describe the structure of the body-wall of *Hydra*.
2. Discuss various modes of locomotion in *Hydra*.
3. Give an account of reproduction and life-history of *Hydra*.
4. Draw a neatly labelled figure of the L.S. through the *Hydra*.
5. Give the structure of cnidoblasts of *Hydra* and write a detailed account on nematocysts.
6. What do you mean by physiological division of labour ? Explain it with reference to *Hydra*.
7. Draw labelled diagrams only :

    (a) T.S. of *Hydra*, (b) Electron-microscopic structure of epithelio-muscular cell, (c) Electron-microscopic structure of cnidoblast.

3

Obelia

The structure of other coelenterates is more complex than that of *Hydra*, therefore, its structure can not be considered as typical of coelenterates. *Hydra* is a fresh water animal where as most coelenterates are marine and colonial. Their life cycle is more complex then that of *Hydra*. *Obelia* is commonly studied as a typical example of marine and colonial coelenterates. Many species of *Obelia* are found but the most common is *Obelia geniculata*.

SYSTEMATIC POSITION

Phylum	-	Coelenterata
Class	-	Hydrozoa
Order	-	Hydroida
Suborder	-	Leptomedusae
Genus	-	*Obelia*

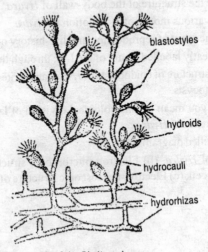

Fig. 3.1. *Obelia* colony.

Habits and Habitat

Obelia is a tree-like branched, marine colonial hydroid coelenterate growing on the surface of sea-weeds, rocks and pilings along the sea-coasts. Colonies appear like whitish or light-brown branched threads, about 30 mm. to several cms in height. The colony arises by budding from a single hydra-like individual, the buds fail to separate and after repeated budding there results a tree-like growth permanently fixed to some object and consisting of numerous members joined to the main stem. The members are known as *zooids*.

EXTERNAL MORPHOLOGY

If a colony of *Obelia* is examined under low power of microscope, it is found to be made up of a root-like horizontal part resembling a basal stem, called *hydrorhiza* which is attached to the substratum. From hydrorhiza

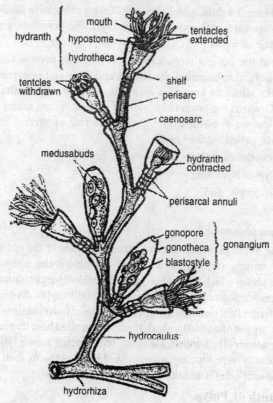

Fig. 3.2 *Obelia.* A part of colony under the microscope.

grows an upright stem called *hydrocaulus (Plural-hydrocauli).* Hydrocaulus and hydrorhiza consist of two distinct layers.

(a) Perisarc. It is a transparent, tough outer layer, yellow in colour, of horny consistency. It is not composed of cells but is a cuticular secretion of the ectodermal cells. The *perisarc* is tubular in shape and is at first in contact with the ectoderm but afterwards becomes separated from it by a small space, except at regular intervals. This condition is acquited secondarily, as during its formation it is in contact with ectoderm but, when it thickens, ectoderm withdraws except at some places. In some parts, perisarc is ringed. Perisarc serves as a protective layer and gives support to the branches having zooids.

(b) Coenosarc. Fibrous processes connect the perisarc with coenosarc. It is an inner, granular layer. It is hollow and its tubular cavity is continued into cavities of polyps, thus, forming a part of *gastrovascular cavity.* There is a fluid, which shows flickering movement similar to that of cilia. Coenosarc consists of an outer layer, the *ectoderm* and an inner layer, the *endoderm.*

From the upright stem, called *hydrocaulus,* several side-branches arise. These side-branches are ringed and their end is expanded into a hydra-like structure known as *hydranth* or *polyp.* Hydranth is a kind of *zooid.* Towards the proximal region of the colony are found cylindrical bodies known as *blastostyles.* These give rise to several small lateral offshoots, called *medusa buds.*

Thus, *Obelia* colony is *trimorphic,* having

(a) Polyp or hydranth;

(b) Blastostyle, and

(c) Medusa.

Polymorphism

Due to the presence of three types of zooids or the individuals, the *Obelia* colony (trimorphic) is said to exhibit the phenomenon of polymorphism which is correlated with the colonial organization of *Obelia.* The phenomenon of polymorphism is essentially one of division of labour i.e., different functions are assigned to different individuals rather than to parts of organs of one individual. It may be recalled here that in *Obelia* the feeding zooids (Hydranths), asexually reproducing zooids (Blastostyles), and sexually reproducing zooids (Medusae) perform their respective functions for *Obelia* and thus exhibit division of labour.

Hydranth or Polyp

It is a nutrient polyp which in its essential structure resembles *Hydra* very much. Under the high power microscope, the polyp looks a hollow case of yellowish colour. It is joined to the main branch by a small stalk. At its distal end it carries an expanded cone-like *manubrium* or *hypostome* which measures about one third of the polyp. The *mouth* is situated at the tip of the manubrium. At the base of the manubrium are twenty four solid *tentacles* which are arranged in a circle. The manubrium is hollow; its cavity opens out by mouth while on the other side, it is continuous with the gastrovascular cavity. The mouth is elastic and capable of great dilation and contraction. It serves both for ingestion and egestion, there being no anus in this animal.

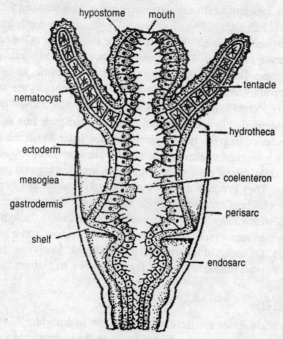

Fig. 3.3 Vertical section of hydranth of *Obelia*.

The perisarc, covering the polyp, forms a cup-like structure called the *hydrotheca* which is transparent and perfectly colourless. The hydrotheca forms a sort of circular *shelf* near its proximal end on which rests the polyp. Normally the polyp remains extended out of the manubrium contract rapidly and are almost completely withdrawn into the hydrotheca.

Histology

As seen under light microscope in longitudinal section, the body wall of the hydranth is seen to consist of two layers of cells :

(a) the outer *ectoderm* or *epidermis*.

(b) the inner *endoderm* or *gastrodermis*,

Separating these layers is a delicate membrane called *mesogloea* or supporting lamella. The hypostome also consists of these two layers of cells. The layers of polyps are continued as coenosarc. The other zooids are also made up of the same layers described above.

Ectoderm is thin and is made up of columnar epithelio-muscular cells. The cells are conical in shape. Their narrow inner ends are prolonged into involuntary muscle fibres arranged longitudinally between epidermis and mesogloea. Interstitial cells may be present in the space between the narrow ends of ectodermal cells. But according to *Grove* and *Newell* the interstitial cells are completely absent. Nematocysts are also present in the ectoderm which act as organs of offence and defence. They are *basitrichous isorhizas* type. These are characterised by an oval capsule, an open long thread bearing spines but without a butt. The nematocysts are specially abundantly present in the tentacles where they constitute annular batteries.

Endodermal cells are large and glandular and their free ends have pseudopodia or flagella, the movement of the latter cause the entry of food particles into the coelenteron (enteron). These are known as musculo-nutritive cells. Gland cells with granular protoplasm are also present in endoderm. They produce digestive enzymes. Tentacles and hypostome also have a layer of unstriated muscle fibres lying between ectoderm and mesoglea which helps in rapid contraction of tentacles. In hypostome, muscle lying transversely serves to contract the cavity and act antagonistically to the action of longitudinal muscle fibres. A nerve net is present on both the sides of the mesogloea. It is formed by large, branched *nerve cells.*

Blastostyle

The blastostyles are developed when the hydrocaulus has attained its full length. They are generally produced on the lower part of the colony in the axil of the branches that bear polyps. The blastostyle is a club-shaped zooid without mouth and tentacles. It is hollow and its cavity is continuous below with that of the rest of the colony. It is enclosed in a cylindrical expansion of the perisarc, the *gonotheca.*

The blastostyle serve to produce the third type of zooids, i.e., the medusae. This occurs by budding. The medusae ultimately get constricted off from the blastostyle and become free inside the gonotheca. The gonotheca develops at its tip an aperture, the *gonopore,* and medusae

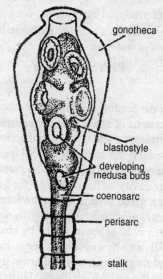

Fig. 3.4. *Obelia.* A blastostyle.

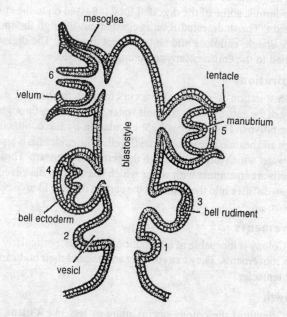

Fig. 3.5. *Obelia.* Development of medusa from a blastostyle.

escape into the sea through it. They are probably expelled through the gonopore by currents produced by rhythmic contractions of the polyps.

The blastostyle, gonotheca and the medusae buds are collectively called the *gonangium* or *gonanth.*

PHYSIOLOGY

Nutrition

The polyps are the feeding zooids. They supply food to the entire colony. The food consists of small living organisms. They are captured with the help of nematocysts and brought to the mouth by tentacles as in *Hydra.* The annuli round the stalks of the polyps give them sufficient flexibility to move in water in pursuit of food. A part of the food is digested in the gastrovascular cavity of the polyps by the action of the digestive juices secreted by the gland cells of the gastrodermis. This is called the *intercellular* or *extracellular* digestion. The partly digested food circulates in the gastrovascular cavity of entire colony by beating of the flagella of the gastrodermal cells and by convulsive peristaltic contractions of the polyps. It is ingested from the gastrovascular cavity by the pseudopodia of the gastrodermal cells in which it is digested in much the same way as in *Amoeba.* This is known as the *intracellular digestion.* From the gastrodermis, some of the digested food is passed on to the epidermis by diffusion. The undigested food is egested out through the mouth of the polyp. Starch, cellulose and chitin are not digested. The digested food is supplied to the entire colony including blastostyle.

Respiration

Respiration is aerobic and occurs through the general surface. The cavity of the entire colony contains water, which enters through the mouth of the polyps. This water is kept circulating by the contractions of the polyps and beating of gastrodermal flagella. The epidermis is also in contact with water which diffuses through the permeable perisarc. Thus, almost all the cells are in contact with water which has oxygen dissolved in it. This oxygen diffuses into the cells and the carbon dioxide likewise diffuses out of them.

Movements

Colony is incapable of locomotion. Its zooids, particularly the polyps, show movements. They can contract and expand their body and can bend their tentacles.

Growth

Growth of the colony occurs more or less like a plant. It involves spreading of the branches of hydrorhiza along the substratum, development of new hydrocauli from the hydrorhiza and formation of new zooids on the branches arising from the hydrocauli. It is to be noted that until a polyp is developed at the end of a branch, the latter does not produce the next branch. Blastostyles grow by budding in the axils of the older branches of a full-grown hydrocaulus. The stimulus leading to blastostyle formation is not clear.

Excretion

Elimination of nitrogenous waste materials takes place by diffusion through the general body surface.

Behaviour

The polyps are sensitive to stimuli. They respond to touch and unfavourable chemicals by contraction.

Osmoregulation

The colony has no problem of osmoregulation as the sea-water is almost as dense as the cell contents. As the sea provides almost a uniform environment throughout the year and there is no dessication, *Obelia* colony does not experience unfavourable periods and is capable of indefinite survival.

MEDUSA

The medusae are the reproductive zooids, some produce eggs and others produce sperms, *i.e.,* the sexes are separate. Each medusa, when

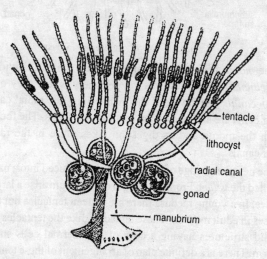

Fig. 3.6. *Obelia*. A medusa in oral view.

fully mature is a saucer-shaped structure. The outer convex side is called the *ex-umbrella* while the concave inner side is known as the *sub-umbrella*. The attachment of the medusa with the blastostyle is by the exumbrellar surface. From the centre of the sub-umbrella hangs a process called *manubrium*, which bears foursided *mouth* at its tip.

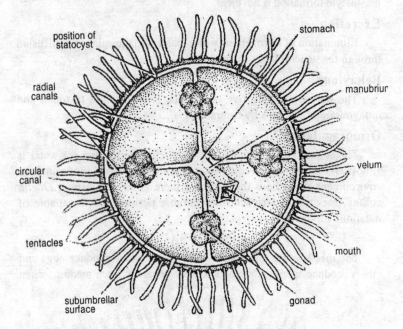

Fig. 3.7. *Obelia*. An everted medusa.

The *mouth* leads into the enteric cavity which is divided into four *radial canals* running towards the periphery where they open into the *circular canal*. The cavity of the manubrium, the radial canals and the circular canal are all lined by the gastrodermal cells. The food is ingested through the mouth and its digestion takes place in the radial and the circular canals.

The peripheral edge of the umbrella is produced into a narrow inward fold called the *velum*. From the margin of the velum arise a large number of tentacles. In a young medusa there are sixteen tentacles but their number increases in adult medusa. These tentacles, like the tentacles of the polyp, are solid structures having a core of endodermal cells surrounded by ectoderm. There is a definite plan of arrangement of these tentacles around the velum. In the young medusa (when there are only 16 tentacles), they are arranged in four groups, each group having 4 tentacles. The four tentacles placed against the four radial canals are the *per-radial tentacles*. Bisecting the four angles between the per-radials, are the four *inter-radii* having the *inter-radial tentacles*. The radii bisecting the inter-radii are the *ad-radii* having *ad-radial tentacles*. Thus there are four per-radial, four inter-radial and eight ad-radial tentacles.

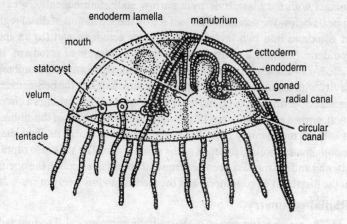

Fig. 3.8 *Obelia.* Medusa in section.

At the base of eight ad-radial tentacles, a few interstitial cells get collected. These cells form a sort of reservoir of cells which form the statocysts. In the basal part these cells contain calcareous particles, *otoliths* or *otocysts*. These cells are also provided with hair-like processes of sensory cells. These organs were previously supposed to be auditory organs. Now they are thought to be co-ordinating or balancing organs which help to maintain the equilibrium.

Histology

Microscopically the structure of medusa resembles that of the hydranth polyp. It consists of the outer epidermis and inner gastrodermis with mesogloea in between the two. At the tip of the manubrium the gastrodermis is continuous with the epidermis. The whole of the ex-umbrellar and sub-umbrellar surfaces are covered by the epidermis while the cavity of the manubrium and the inner radial canals and circular canal are lined by the gastrodermis. The velum is made up of two layers of epidermis with a core of mesogloea. The epidermis has a large number of stinging capsules. On the radial canals are usually present the gonads, one on each canal.

DEVELOPMENT OF MEDUSA FROM BLASTOSTYLE

The cavity of blastostyle pushes out the coenosarc forming a simple diverticulum. Soon it enlarges to form a small sac with a cavity enclosed by two layers of ectoderm. This diverticulum increases in dimension at its extremity and forms a small vesicle enclosed by ectoderm, mesogloea, and endoderm. It also has enteron of blastostyle. The medusa remains in contact with the blastostyle by a narrow stalk. Subsequently, a cavity appears below the subumbrellar surface by the separation of distal region of ectoderm into two layers : (a) an outer ectoderm and (b) an inner ectoderm. There is a cavity between these two layers of ectoderm. It is called *bell-rudiment.* It grows in size and assumes the form of sub-umbrellar cavity with the manubrium lying in the centre. Later on the bell-ectoderm (outer ectoderm) breaks up and the remaining part of it constitutes a circular shelf, termed as *velum,* projecting inwards from the margin of the umbrella. It is quite rudimentary here. When the medusa acquires its final shape, mouth breaks through the apex of the manubrium. The stalk also ruptures later on and the medusa becomes free and comes out through the opening at the distal end of gonotheca, and the medusa swims freely in sea-water.

Radial symmetry

The medusa, like polyp, is also radially symmetrical. The four radial canals mark the four principal radii, called *per-radii* and the tentacles lying against the four radial canals are *per-radial tentacles.* Between any two per radii is the *inter-radius* with *inter-radial tentacles.* Bisecting between a per-radius and adjacent interradius is the *ad-radius* and then the *sub-radius.* Thus there are four per-radii, four inter-radii, eight ad-radii and sixteen sub-radii. In *Obelia,* the radial canals, the angles of the mouth and four of the sixteen tentacles of the young medusa are per-radial, four other tentacles are inter-radial and the remaining eight tentacles bearing the lithocysts are ad-radial.

PHYSIOLOGY

Movement

The *Obelia* colony is fixed and does not show any bodily movement from one place to another. The polyps can control and expand their body and can bend their tentacles.

The medusae, on the other hand, float passively in water and are drifted along the water currents. They also swim actively by muscular contraction. The impulses, originating in the nerves of the umbrella bring about muscular contraction. By rhythmic contraction and expansion of umbrella, the water in the sub-umbrellar cavity is propelled behind and the animal moves ahead with a series of jerks. The contraction of the bell is brought about by the contraction of the ectodermal muscle-tail which are better developed along the sub-umbrellar surface, specially along the surface where they form a muscle ring. The waves of contraction start from the sub-umbrellar surface and fade towards the exumbrellar surface where they are completely absent. The bell opens mainly by the elastic mesoglea and to some extent by the contraction of the muscle-tails in the middle of the upper surface. During swimming, the body of the medusa may be tilted, thrown aside or more often turned inside out so that the sub-umbrellar surface becomes outer and convex with the manubrium arising from its apex.

Nutrition

The medusa is carnivorous, feeding on nematodes, insects, crustanceans, small worms etc. The prey is captured by the tentacles with the help of nematocysts and ingested by the highly contractile mouth. The digestion takes place in stomach. It is both extracellular and intracellular. The digested food is distributed to the different parts of the medusa through radial and circular canals.

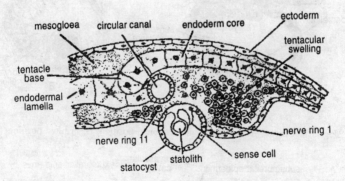

Fig. 3.9. *Obelia.* L.S. of the base of an adradial tentacle of medusa.

Nervous system

The nerve cells of the epidermis and gastrodermis are present on either side of mesoglea to form nerve nets. However, the nerve cells are specially concentrated along the margin of the umbrella to form two circular nerve rings on either side just below and above the base of the velum. The upper ex-umbrellar nerve ring supplies the tentacles while the lower nerve ring supplies the sub-umbrellar musculature and the statocysts.

Sense organs

The medusa has eight marginal receptor organs situated at the bases of the eight adradial tentacles on the sub-umbrellar surface, just inside the bell-margin. Each consists of a minute and fluid-filled ectodermal sac, called the *statocyst* or *marginal vesicle*. Its cavity contains a movable round particle of calcium carbonate, called *statolith* or *otolith*, secreted by a large cell, termed *lithocyte*. The wall of the statocyst is made of epithelial cells, which are sensory towards the bell-margin, being connected basally with nerve cells. The free inner ends of these sensory cells bear fine protoplasmic sensory processes which arch over the statolith.

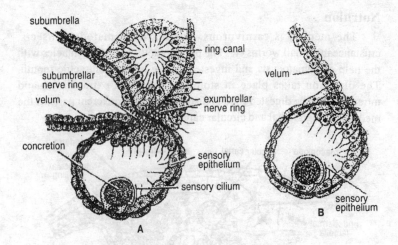

Fig. 3.10 *Obelia.* Statocysts : A. in horizontal position; B. in tilted position.

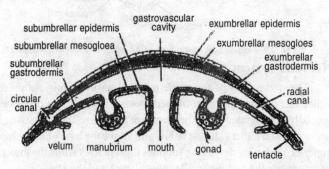

Fig 3.11 *Obella.* A vertical section of medusa showing gonads.

The statocysts are considered to be organs of *equilibrium* and muscular *coordination*. Their presence in medusae is associated with their active free-swimming habit. During swimming if the body becomes tilted, the statolith falls over the tilted side against the processes of sensory cells which become stimulated. In this way, nerve impulse in created and transmitted to the nerve ring. As a result, the muscle tails of the stimulated side contract more rapidly and the medusa is brought again into the normal position.

Reproduction

In *Obelia*, the asexual reproduction takes place by budding as a result of which *hydranths* and *blastostyles* are formed. The blastostyles bud-off medusae which are the sexual zooids of *Obelia* because the gonads are found in four groups in each of them. The gonads of a medusa are of the same sex.

Each medusa of *Obelia* is unisexual i.e. sperms and ova are produced in separate individuals. The *gonads* are situated on the radial canals in the sub-umbrellar surface. Actually, each gonad arises as an outgrowth from the wall of the radial canal. It has ectoderm, endoderm and mesoglea as well as an extension of the coelenteron. In fact, the *oogonia* and *spermatogonia* both originate in the ectoderm of the hypostome or manubrium from there they move into the endoderm and later they gradually migrate to the gonads in the radial canals. Before the gonads mature, they reach the endoderm and come to lie between the ectoderm and mesoglea where their maturation takes place. The sperms and ova come out by rupturing the ectoderm and swim freely in the sea water.

LIFE HISTORY

Fertilization

In *Obelia*, always cross fertilization takes place. The ova are fertilized in the body of the female medusa or in the sea water. The sperms come towards the ova along with the water current.

Development

The zygote undergoes holoblastic and repeated equal cleavages forming a *blastula* which is hollow. The cavity of blastula is called *blastocoel* which is surrounded by a single layer of cells. Soon the cells start separating from the wall of the blastoderm and collect in the blastocoel due to which it becomes completely filled up by them. Thus, a solid gastrula or *stereogastrula* is formed as a result of *delamination* and multipolar immigration of the ectodermal cells. The outer layer of cells of the gastrula forms the ectoderm of the adult while the inner layer of cells forms its endoderm. After some time, cilia appear in the cells of ectoderm. Simultaneously, a *colenteron* in the centre is formed by the delamination of the endodermal cells. The gastrula in this stage is known as *planula larva.*

Metamorphosis

After leading a free swimming life for some time, the planula larva settles down and attaches itself by its broad anterior end to some object and the process of metamorphosis starts in it. Its anterior end form the basal disc by which the animal remains attached to the substratum and the posterior end forms the manubrium. A mouth is formed at the free end of the manubrium around which a circlet of tentacles is present. In this way a simple polyp-like structure is formed which is called *hydrula stage.* The basal part of hydrula elongates to form the *hydrorhiza* from which vertical and lateral branches arise forming the adult *Obelia* colony. Again the medusa buds arise on the blastostyles of this colony and start the sexual generation.

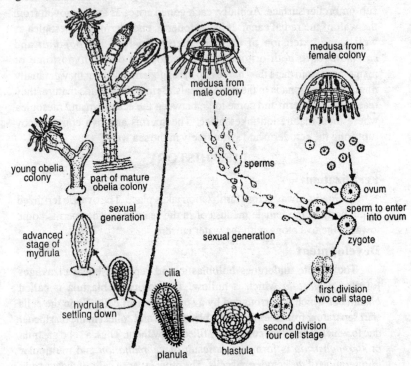

Fig. 3.12 Life-cycle of *Obelia.*

The free swimming medusae are very important in a fixed animal like *Obelia* because they help in its far and wide distribution so that more facilities may be available to it.

Alternation of Generations or Metagenesis

The life-cycle of *Obelia* colony described above gives the impression that alternation of generations or metagenesis takes place. The sedentary colonial asexual hydroid phase gives rise by budding to medusae which represent the sexual generation. The gonads of medusa produce sperms and ova. The fertilized ovum ultimately gives rise to planula larva which gives rise to *Obelia* colony. In other words the sexual medusa gives rise to asexual colony by sexual method. This alternation of generations or metagenesis confers upon the species not only genetical advantage but also ecological advantage. When each asexual and sexual form has a large reproductive capacity, one sexual, the other asexual, the species has the less chance of being eliminated due to predation or competition. However, in the strict sense the life-cycle of *Obelia* does not represent a true case of alternation of generations which occurs in the life-cycle of certain plants such as Ferns, the asexual diploid (2n) phase forms haploid (n) sexual phase by its single cell. But in the case of *Obelia*, both the sedentary asexual colonial polypoid generation and mobile sexual medusoid generation are diploid (only the sperm and ova produced in the gonad of medusa having brief existence are haploid.) Moreover, the medusa (sexual phase) is not derived from a single cell of the asexual phase but is formed by many cells of the blastostyle by budding. Hence the life-cycle of *Obelia* though apparently seems to represent alternation of generations does not do so in *strict sense*. This particular phenomenon with alternation between two diploid phases is termed metagenesis.

COMPARISON OF POLYP AND MEDUSA

The polyp and medusa of *Obelia* are two different kinds of zooids which differ from each other in the structure, shape and other respects. These differences are according to their varying functions. The polyps are nutritive and the medusae are reproductive in function. Thus they are different in shape according to their functions. Their basic structure is, however, the same because of which some similarities are also found in them. Therefore, the comparison between polyp and medusa can be done only on the basis of similarities and dissimilarities in them.

Resemblances

Apparently there seems to be no similarity between the polyp and the medusa. Actually, however, the two are homologous structures, being

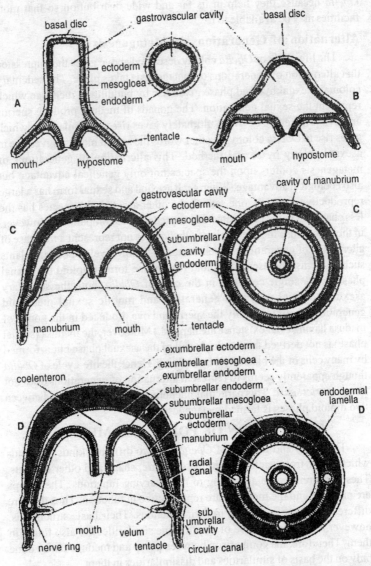

Fig. 3.13.   Diagram illustrating the derivation of the medusa from the polyp. A-Polyp in L.S., A'-Polyp from with extended tenacular region, C-Vertical and C' transverse section of form with tentacular region extended into the form of a bell; D-Vertical and D' transverse seection of medusa.

built on the same fundamental plan. Resemblance between the two is so close that one can be easily derived from the other. An inverted polyp at once assumes the medusoid form if its region of tentacles is pulled out and manubrium is pushed up. This, together with the thickening of mesogloea, especially on the upper side, brings the walls of the polyp together so that they meet everywhere to form the *gastrodermal lamella* except along the radial and circular canals. Thus, we find that the manubrium, subumbrellar surface, exumbrellar surface and tentacles of the medusa correspond to the manubrium, oral side, aboral side or foot, and tentacles of the polyp respectively. Moreover, the polyp and the medusa have the same layers, which occupy the same relative positions in both, the epidermis covering the outer surface, the gastrodermis lining the cavities and the mesogloea lying between the two. In both, the gastrovascular cavity has a single outlet and both have solid tentacles bearing cnidoblasts. The nature of food and modes of capturing and digesting it are also similar in the two. Finally, both arise as buds on the colony and show radial symmetry.

Differences Between polyp and medusa

Polyp	Medusa
1. Body of the polyp is long and cylindrical.	1. Body of the medusa is short and umbrella-like.
2. Polyp is a fixed zooid.	2. Medusa is a free-living zooid in the mature stage.
3. Polyp is enclosed in a transparent protective covering, the hydrotheca.	3. Medusa is without any covering.
4. The mouth of the polyp is circular and lies at the upper end of the upright manubrium.	4. The mouth of the medusa is four-sided and lies at the lower end of the hanging manubrium.
5. The tentacles of the polyp are situated at the base of the manubrium.	5. The tentacle of the medusa are situated at the margin of the umbrella.
6. There is no velum.	6. Velum, which is a small inward projection all along the margin, is present.
7. The gastrovascular cavity is a single spacious cavity occupying the whole of the body of the polyp.	7. The gastrovascular cavity is restricted and differentiated into the cavity of the manubrium, radial canals and a circular canal.

8. There are no endodermal lamellae.	8. There is an endoderm lamella between radial canals in each quadrant.
9. The mesogloea is almost of uniform thickness throughout	9. The mesogloea is much thicker on the exumbrella side than on the other side.
10. The nervous system is poorly developed, consisting only of a double nerve-net	10. The nervous system is much better developed, consisting of consisting of a double nerve-ring and a double nerve-net.
11. There are no sense organs.	11. There are eight sense organs, the statocysts.
12. The polyp feeds and protects the colony.	12. The medusa brings about sexual reproduction and dispersal of the colony.
13. Polyps are produced directly on the hydrocauli.	13. Medusae are produced on the blastostyles and not directly on hydrocauli.
14. Polyp belongs to the asexual generation.	14. Medusa belongs to the sexual generation.

Medusa shows a distinct morphological advancement over the polyp in having sense organs and nerve-ring in the nervous system; almost an independent muscular tissue; differentiation of gastrovascular cavity into region like gullet, stomach, radial canals and circular canal; gonads for sexual reproduction; and free-swimming life.

Polyp versus *Hydra*

Polyp of *Obelia* resembles *Hydra* in form, structure and mode of feeding. The two, however, differ in many respects. The more obvious differences are tabulated below -

Comparison of the Structure of *Hydra* and *Obelia*

Hydra	*Obelia*
1. *Hydra* is a solitary animal but because of the presence of buds, sometimes it may also be branched. Later these buds separate from the parent and lead independent lives.	1. *Óbelia* is a colonial animal. It appears like a branched tree because the lateral branches do not separate from it.

2. It is semi-sedentary and remains temporarily attached on aquatic plants, stones or the wall of the pond. It can be occasionally seen floating in water. The *basal disc* helps in attaching it to the substratum.

2. It is fully sedentary and ramins permanently attached to marine plants and rocks. It is attached to the substratum by means of *hydrorhiza.*

3. Polymorphism is absent in it. Only polyp or hydranth stage is found.

3. It is polymorphic animal which is found in three forms.
   (a) Polyp or hydranth
   (b) Blastostyle
   (c) Medusa.

4. There is no covering around it

4. The polyp is enclosed in a conical cup-shaped *hydrotheca.*

5. Its body is long and cylindrical, and its lower end closes to form the basal disc by which it remains attached to the substratum.

5. The polyp is long and wine glass-shaped. Its both the ends are open and lower end is connected with the hydro-caulus through a circular shelf.

6. The free distal end of *Hydra* is conical and called *hypostome.* There is a mouth at its apex.

6. The hypostome of polyp forms its 1/3 part and a mouth is present at its apex.

7. There are 6 to 10 tentacles around the mouth on the hypostome. These tentacles are hollow.

7. The number of tentacles around mouth is about 25 and they are solid.

8. A thin transparent membranous cuticle forms the outer covering of the body of *Hydra.* The perisarc is absent.

8. The cuticle is absent in *Obelia* and the whole colony is covered by a thick and tough *perisarc.*

9. The body wall of *Hydra* is made up of two layers the outer *ectoderm* and the inner *endoderm.*

9. The same two layers are found in *Obelia.*

10. A non-cellular *mesoglea* is present between these two layers.

10. The mesoglea is also non-cellular.

11. It is not so in *Hydra.*

11. The two layers of the polyp are united with the two similar layers of the hydrocaulus.

12. A gastrovascular cavity is present but it is closed at the lower or basal end.

12. The gastrovascular cavity of the polyp is in communication behind with the coenosarc of the hydrocaulus and the hydrorhiza.

13. The following seven types of cells are found in the outer layer (ectoderm).
    (a) Epithelio-muscular cells
    (b) Interstitial cells
    (c) Nematoblasts
    (d) Sensory cells
    (e) Nerve cells
    (f) Gland cells
    (g) Reproductive cells.

13. Only five types of cells are found in the outer layer (ectoderm) of the polyp. The gland cells and reproductive cells are absent in it.

14. The nutritive and reproductive activities both are done by the *Hydra*. The blastostyles and medusae are absent in it.

14. In *Obelia*, the polyp is only nutritive form which supplies food to the colony. It has not reproductive function. The blastostyles (asexual) and medusae (sexual) are the reproductive forms.

Hydra and *Obelia* both are the members of the Order Hydroidea, Class Hydrozoa and Phylum Coelenterata, by which it is apparent that there should be many similarities between them, however, there are also many dissimilarities in them. The following differences are met within their life histories.

Differences between the reproduction and life histories of *Hydra* and *Obelia*

Hydra	*Obelia*
(A) Reproduction	
1. The reproduction is *Hydra* takes place by two methods : (a) Asexual (b) Sexual.	1. Only sexual reproduction occurs in *Obelia* although the whole colony grows by asexual method of budding.
2. The asexual reproduction mostly occurs by *budding*. *Hydra* is also capable of fission	2. In asexual reproduction, the colony increases in size and new *zooids* are formed which

and regeneration. The bud separates from the parent body after sometime and leads an independent life.

3. The sexual reproduction takes place by the formation of gametes.

4. The gonads are formed in the polyp condition in *Hydra*. Therefore, the polyp also acts as a reproductive zooids.

5. *Hydra* is mostly bisexual but unisexual individuals also occur.

6. The gonads of *Hydra* are temporary structures which are formed only during breeding season.

7. The gonads are formed from the interstitial cells of the ectoderm and project out on the body wall. There is only a layer of ectoderm on their outer side.

8. The number of gonads is not definite.

9. The male gonads or testes are found in the anterior region of the body while the female gonads or ovaries are situated in the posterior region near the base.

10. The reproductive cells are formed by the division of interstitial cells and collect together to form gonads.

11. The mature female gametes do not come out in water from the parent body.

do not separate from parent colony.

3. The gametes are also formed in the *Obelia*.

4. The gonads are formed in the medusa form in *Obelia*.

5. The Medusa of *Obelia* is always unisexual.

6. The gonads of *Obelia* are permanent structures.

7. The gonads are formed on the subumbrellar surface from the ectoderm and are situated in the mesogloea between the ecto- and endoderm.

8. Only four gonads are present is a medusa.

9. The gonads in medusa are of one sex only i.e. either male or female and are radial.

10. The reproductive cells are formed in the ectoderm of the manubrium and migrate to mesogloea to form gonads.

11. The male and female gametes both separate from the parent body after maturation and swim freely in water.

(B) Life History

12. The fertilization is external and completed in the ovum while attached to the parent body.

12. The fertilization is external and takes place in the ovum swimming in the water.

13. The development of the zygote takes place in the parent body.

13. The development of zygote takes place in water.

14. The cleavage of the zygote is holoblastic and equal.

14. The cleavage of the zygote is also holoblastic and equal.

15. A solid ball-like morula is formed as a result of division. Later with the formation of blastocoel, a blastula (having eight blastomeres) is formed.

15. A solid morula is formed by division. It later changes into a single layered hollow blastula.

16. As a result of delamination the blastula changes into a two-layered gastrula.

16. By the process of delamination, the blastula changes into a solid gastrula.

17. A double layered cyst is secreted by the outer layer of the gastrula around the embryo. The outer cyst wall is thick, hard and spiny but the inner cyst wall is thin and gelatinous.

17. Cilia are formed on the ectodermal cells of the gastrula as a result of which an oval, ciliated *planula* larva is formed.

18. In the encysted condition, the embryo detaches from the parent body and lies in the mud of the pond and remains in dormant condition.

18. The planula larva leads a free swimming life and does not rest.

19. The cyst ruptures with the onset of favourable conditions in spring season and a small *Hydra* comes out of it which grows into the adult.

19. After leading a free swimming life, the planula larva attaches to some substratum and transforms by growing into an adult colony. The planula first changes into *hydrula* which forms the different zooids of the colony by budding.

20. Alternation of generations is not found in the life history of *Hydra* because only one form of zooids is found in it.

20. Alternation of generations or metagenesis occurs in the life history of *Obelia*. A regular alternation of asexual and sexual stages is found in it.

Revision Questions

1. Describe the various types of zooids found in the *Obelia* colony.

2. Describe the structure, development, physiology and reproduction of *Obelia* medusa.

3. How can a medusa be derived from a polyp ?

4. What is meant by metagenesis ? Explain it with reference to the life-cycle of *Obelia*.

5. Draw labelled diagrams of the following : (a) Medusa of *obelia*, (b) Life cycle of *Obelia*, (c) V.S. of hydranth of *Obelia*, (d) *Obelia* colony.

6. Define polymorphism and discuss the phenomenon by describing some important examples selected from phylum Coelenterata.

7. Give an account of structure of *Obelia* and compare it with that of *Hydra*.

8. Explain that, "Striking as the differences between a polyp and a medusa, they are strictly homologous structures.

9. Write short notes on : (a) Metagenesis, (b) Medusa, (c) Hydranth, (d) Planula, (e) Metagenesis, (f) Polymorphism.

4

Aurelia

Aurelia is a common jelly fish. Animals known as "Jelly fishes" are kept in class Scyphozoa. Probably the name is derived due to the presence of jelly-like substance forming most of their body. The word fish attached to it is unsuitable because these animals have no connection with fishes except that both are found in water.

SYSTEMATIC POSITION

Phylum	-	Coelenterata
Class	-	Scyphozoa
Order	-	Semaeostomae
Genus	-	*Aurelia*

Habits and Habitat

Aurelia is almost cosmopolitan in distribution. It is found in tropical and temperate seas. It inhibits the coastal waters, generally remaining at or near the surface. It is generally seen floating separately or in groups, by rhythmic contractions of the bell. It is often found cast upon the sea shore and is recognized by its gelatinous saucer-shaped umbrella, 3-4 inches in diameter and by four red or purple horse-shoe shaped gonads in its centre.

MORPHOLOGY

Shape and Size

Aurelia has a flattened, saucer-shaped body often referred to as the umbrella or bell. It generally measures upto four inches. The dorsal (exumbrellar) surface of the bell is convex and the ventral (subumbrellar) surface is concave. The umbrella is transparent.

Colouration

The umbrella is bluish-white in colour through which red or pink gonads are visible.

Symmetry

It possesses *tetramerous radial symmetry* i.e. the body parts are symmetrically arranged around the oral-aboral axis in four or some multiple of four.

EXTERNAL CHARACTERS

The body is very much like that of hydromedusa having the form of an umbrella, a convex *exumbrellar* side and a concave *subumbrellar* side.

In the centre of the subumbrellar side is a short and inconspicuous *manubrium*. The manubrium have a square mouth at its free end. From each corner of mouth hangs down a long, tapering much frilled and delicate process, the *oral arm*. Each arm has a ventral ciliated groove leading into the mouth. The edges of the arms have a large number of nematocysts. The angles of mouth and the oral arms lie along per-radii. Midway between two adjacent per-radii is an inter-radius. Between each per-radius and its adjacent inter-radius is an ad-radius on either side.

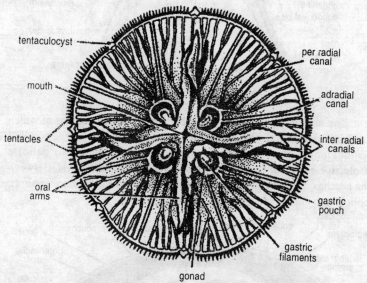

Fig. 4.1. *Aurelia aurita.*

Four round apertures are present between the oral arms, a little away from the mouth, on subumbrellar surface. These apertures open into *subgenital pits*. Each pit is in the form of hollow and shallow depression and lies beneath gonad. Their function is uncertain. Four pink or red horseshoe *shaped* gonads present just above the subgenital pits. They are visible through the transparent umbrella. They are endodermal in origin.

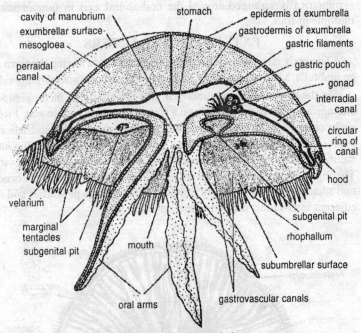

Fig. 4.2. *Aurelia aurita*.Lateral view.

The margin is indented with eight equally-spaced notches of which four are per-radial and four inter-radial. A sensory organ called *tentaculocyst* or *rhopalium* is situated in each notch.Two delicate protective *marginal lappets* are found over each tentaculocyst. Between the notches, the edge of umbrella is fringed by a row of numerous, short, hollow *marginal tentacles*, set closely together.

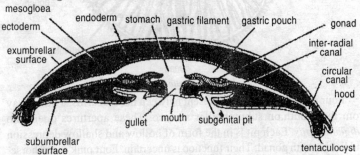

Fig. 4 3 *Aurelia aurita*.V.S. (diagrammatic).

The tentaculocysts, marginal lappets and tentacles all are attached to an extremely flexible fold called *velarium* on the umbrella. A true velum like that of *Obelia,* is absent. It differs from true velum in having gastrodermal canal running into it.

Histology

The main types of tissues their arrangement in *Aurelia* are practically similar to those found in other hydrozoan medusa (*Obelia*).

1. Epidermis

The exposed part of umbrella i.e., exumbrellar as well as subumbrellar surfaces, velarium, manubrium, oral arms, marginal tentacles etc. are covered with epidermis. The epidermis also lines subgenital pits. It consists of epithelial cells on the exumbrellar surface while the subumbrellar surface contains epithelio-muscular cells besides sensory cells, nerve cells, gland cells and cnidoblasts. It forms sensory epithelium for the sense organs. The muscle processes of the epidermal cells are cross-striated at certain places and smooth at others.

The cnidoblasts occur on the oral arms, ex-and sub-umbrellar surfaces, marginal tentacles and gastric filaments. There are two types of cnidoblasts :

(a) Atrichous isorhiza. The capsule is oval or elongate and the thread is open at the tip. The butt and spines are absent.

(b) Heterotrichous microbasic euryteles. The capsule is small and the thread is open. The thread remains covered by minute spines. The butt is small and its distal dilated portion bears unequal spines.

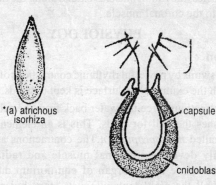

*(a) atrichous isorhiza

capsule

cnidoblast

Fig. 4.4. *Aurelia.* Types of nematocysts.

2. Gastrodermis

All the parts of digestive cavity viz. gullet, stomach, gastric pouches, radial canals and circular canals are lined by gastrodermal cells. It consists of columnar epithelial cells which are flattened throughout to maintain a current of water. Gland cells are also present but nerve cells and muscle processes are absent. The gastric filaments possess the cnidoblasts but they are absent from the gastrodermis.

3. Mesogloea

Between the epidermis and endodermis is a very thick layer of jelly-like mesogloea. It forms the main bulk of the bell. It is not structureless like the mesogloea of *Hydra* or *Obelia* as, it contains elastic fibres and free wandering amoeboid cells. These cells are derived from ectomesodermal cells. Such a mesogloea is more or less like connective tissue and is more accurately termed *collenchyme.*

Muscular system

Musculature in *Aurelia* is practically wholly epidermal and confined to the subumbrellar surface. It is formed by the muscle processes of epidermal epithelial-muscle cells. The muscle processes form strong longitudinal muscles in the tentacles, manubrium and axes of the oral arms. The subumbrellar muscles are striated and arranged in a strong broad and circular peripheral band called the *coronal muscle*. It is composed of regular muscle fibres,each consisting of a complete epidermal cell. The coronal muscle forms the swimming organelle of *Aurelia*. The muscle fibres of coronal muscle and muscle processes of longitudinal tentacle muscles are cross-striated and capable of rapid contraction. Another muscles, the *radial muscles* extend along the main radii from the manubrium to the coronal muscle.

PHYSIOLOGY

Locomotion

Aurelia swims by powerful rhythmic contractions of its body muscles, during which the exumbrellar surface is kept upwards.

The contractions force the water back from the subumbrellar cavity and this pushes the bell forwards. This is an elementary form of jet-propulsion,called *hydropropulsion*.The contractions are brought about by the highly developed coronal muscle and radial muscles. The tentaculocysts serve as the organ of equilibrium during swimming. Removal of all the eight tentaculocysts stops pulsations. When the contractions stop, the body gradually sinks to the bottom. Horizontal movements are brought about by wave action and currents.

Gastrovascular System

The mouth which is situated at the tip of the manubrium leads into a short gullet which opens into a large rectangular *stomach*. The stomach is produced laterally into four gastric pouches which are inter-radial canals in position. At the four corners of the mouth are branched four *per-radial canals* at right angles to each other, and between them are four *inter-radial canals* which are very much branched and end at the *marginal lappets*. Halfway between the per-radial and inter-radial canals are eight unbranched *ad-radial canals*, two of them arising from each gastric pouch. From the inner concave border of each gastric pouch, a number of small thin gastric filaments are given out which form a regular row. Each consists of a fold of endoderm and a central core of mesogloea and bears a large number of nematocysts.

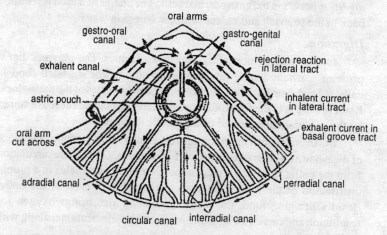

Fig. 4.5. *Aurelia*. Diagrammatic representation of gastrovascular system.

The ad-radial canals open into a *circular canal* running to the margin of the bell. Thus there are 16 canals in total, all of them open into a marginal circular canal. The gullet, stomach with its gastric pouches and all the canals constitute an enteron cavity or gastro-vascular system which is lined with *ciliated endodermal cells*. The beating of the cilia causes the circulation of the fluid. The water drawn into the mouth goes to gullet then into the stomach and gastric pouches and then through the ad-radial canals to the circular canal from where it returns by the branches per-radial canals and inter-radial canals to the exhalent groove of oral arms and from here it goes out. Thus enteron is a gastrovascular cavity.

Food

Aurelia is exclusively carnivorous. The food consists of small marine invertebrates such as worms, crustaceans and small pieces of animals.

Ingestion

By the beating of cilia of the endodermal cells circulates a water current through the gastrovascular cavity or canal system in a definite direction. Water along with the food, is brought into the folds of the oral arms from where it passes into the gullet through the mouth. From there it moves into the stomach and then into the gastric pouches. Here the alive prey is paralysed and killed by the nematocysts of gastric filaments. *Intercellular digestion* is started here by the enzymes containing the juice from the gland cells. From the pouches digested and undigested food, with water current reaches the radial and circular canals where *intracellular digestion* occurs in the gastrodermal cells. The undigested food is returned back to the stomach and escape with the outgoing water.

Digestion

Aurelia secretes most of the digestive enzymes. The enzymes digest proteins, carbohydrates, fats, and even chitin. The digested food is collected and distributed by the wandering amoebocytes of the mesogloea. Reserve food is in the form of fat droplets and glycogen. These are stored by the gastodermal cells and of the gastric filaments.

It is thus clear that the entire gastro-vascular cavity performs functions of digestion as well as circulation of higher animals. The entire circulation from the gullet back into it takes about 20 minutes and helps in a proper distribution of the food substances to the different parts of the body. Besides bringing food, the water circulation also brings oxygen for respiration and carries away waste products, sex elements etc. along with undigested food.

Water circulation

The circulation of water is brought about by the beating of cilia of gastrodermis in definite directions. Water entering mouth passes into stomach, thence to the gastric pouches. From the exhalent channels of the gastric pouch it goes into the ad-radial canals then into the circular canal. Water return from circular canal in the branches of inter-radial and per-radial canals. Inter-radial canals bring the water into the gastric pouches, it flows through the inhalent channel and back to the gullet. Per-radial canals return the water directly into the gullet. Just near the base of grooves of the oral arms, which are exhalent. Thus, water return both ways is eventually passed on the oral grooves. It may be seen that in such a course the incoming water-current is not polluted by the outgoing current.

Respiration

There are no specialized organs for respiration thus entire body surface presumably perform the respiratory function. Respiration is aerobic. The epidermal cells are in contact with surrounding water and the gastrodermal cells are bathed by water current circulating in canal system. Water containing oxygen is diffused into the cells and carbon dioxide is diffused out in the water.

According to some workers, below each gonad on the subumbrellar side is situated a sub-genital pit, in which by rhythmic contractions of umbrella, water enters and constant change of water may be responsible for the process of respiration through general body surface.

Excretion

Nitrogenous waste products are eleminated out by the processes of diffusion from epidermal and gastrodermal surfaces. In the deeper parts of mesogloea these are eleminated by the wandering cells, which ingest them.

NERVOUS SYSTEM

The nervous system is epidermal, simple but formed on a different plan from that of hydroid medusa (*Obelia*). The following structures are found in the nervous system :

(i) Subumbrellar plexus or Main nerve net.

(ii) Rhopalial ganglia.

(i) Subumbrellar Plexus

It is formed of very long bipolar nerve cells and nerve fibres and extends between the ectoderm and upper muscular layer on the subumbrellar surface. It consists of two different and definite plexuses.

(a) *Sub-epidermal plexus* and (b) *Sub-gastrodermal plexus*

The sub-epidermal plexus extends into the manubrium, oral lobes and tentacles while the sub-gastrodermal plexus lies in the wall of gastro-vascular system. The nervous system is much thicker in the radial position. It is much thickened and distinct at the places of per-radii and inter-radii, and situated near the marginal notches and sensory organs. These plexuses control the contractions of the bell.

Besides another diffused nerve plexus occurs in both the subumbrellar and exumbrellar epidermis. It controls the local activities, like feeding and can prevent the contractions of the bell.

(ii) Rhopalial Ganglia

These are aggregation of nerve-cells, one near each sense organ or rhopalium. They are connected with the nerve-nets but, not directly with each other.

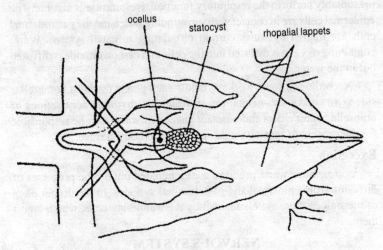

Fig. 4.6. *Aurelia*. Rhopalium (diagrammatic).

There is a ring of nerve cells along the margin of umbrella. It runs along the marginal or circular canals

Sense organs

There are three kinds of sensory organs in *Aurelia* :

1. The sensory tentacles or tentaculocysts
2. Ocelli
3. Sensory Pits.

1. Tentaculocysts

There are eight club-shaped tentaculocysts lying between marginal lappets at the end of inter-radial and per-radial canals. Each tentaculocyst is covered on the outer side by a process of the bell margin known as *hood*. A pad of ciliated sensory epithelial cells is present below the club of tentaculocyst. The circular canal projects into it and thus it is a hollow tentacle lined by gastrodermis. The gastrodermal cells heap up in the distal part of the tentaculocysts as a mass of polygonal cells. Each cell of this mass secretes a calcareous particle called *statolith*. The statolith composed of calcium sulphate mixed with a small amount of calcium phosphate. The epidermis is thickened at the sides and the base of tentaculocyst contain tall sensory cells which are connected with the subumbrellar nerve plexus.

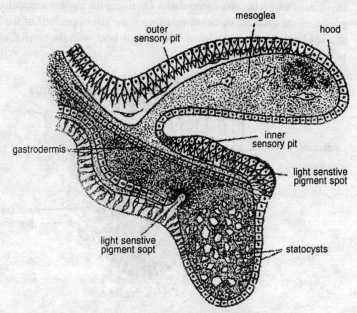

Fig. 4.7.*Aurelia*. Section through hood and sensory organs.

The tentaculocysts are regarded as organs of equilibrium.If these are removed from the animal, it never shows spontaneous movements. If the

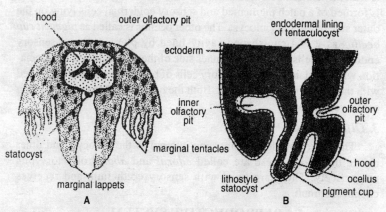

Fig. 4.8. *Aurelia aurita*. A-small portion of edge of umbrella showing relation of tentaculocyst, B- tentaculocyst in vertical section.

bell is tilted the clubs of tentaculocysts press against their sensory pads the cells of which becomes stimulated. On tilting the highest tentaculocyst produces the greatest stimulation. In response the upper half of the bell derives less water than the lower half, at each beat, with the result that the bell automatically rights itself.

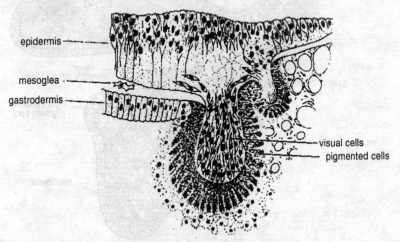

Fig. 4.9. *Aurelia aurita*. Section through ocelli.

2. Ocelli

There are two ocelli, one of them is ectodermal in origin while other is endodermal. The ectodermal ocellus is known as *pigment spot ocellus*.It is formed of a patch pigmented and sensory epidermal cells lying on the outer side of the tentaculocyst. The other ocellus is called as *pigment cup ocellus* as it is a cup-shaped cavity lined by pigmented and sensory endodermal cells, lying on the inner side of the tentaculocyst in association with the statoliths. The sensory cells of both the ocelli are connected with the respective nerve plexus. Both the ocelli are photoreceptor being sensitive to light.

3. Olfactory pits

These are two depressions, one internal to the statocyst and other above the hood. These are called *adoral* and *aboral* olfactory pits respectively. These are lined with sensory epithelium and receives chemical stimuli.

REPRODUCTIVE SYSTEM

Aurelia is *dioecious* or unisexual but they are alike in structure i.e. there is no sexual dimorphism. Four gonads (testes or ovaries) lie interradially on the floor of the gastric pouches. The gonads are horseshoe shaped. Their colour is reddish or pinkish. The gonads are endodermal in their origin. The testes of mature male liberate spermatozoa into the genital pouches from where they pass out through the mouth with the outgoing water. The female gametes or ova are liberated in the genital pouches where they remain till fertilization occur.

Fertilization

Fertilization is effected in the gastro-vascular cavity of female medusa. The spermatozoa from water find their way into the female with the ingoing water current and reach its genital pouch. Here, fertilization takes place. Thus fertilization is *internal*. The zygotes or fertilized eggs pass out with the outgoing water current and get lodged in the grooves of the oral arms of the female. Thus, oral arms serving as temporary brood chambers and development takes place within these chambers.

Cleavage

The zygote undergoes holoblastic but unequal cleavage to produce a solid, ball-like *morula*, The morula changes into a single-layered hollow, closed sphere, the *blastula* by developing a fluid filled central cavity or blastocoel. The blastula undergoes gastrulation by an invagination. Thus a two layered *gastrula* is formed which has as outer layer of ectoderm and inner layer of endoderm enclosing a cavity, the *coelenteron cavity* which has an opening, the *blastopore*. As the invagination progresses, the coelenteron cavity enlarges at the cost of blastocoel which finally disappear. The gastrula elongates and its ectoderm develops cilia. The blastopore is closed. Thus the embryo becomes a free swimming oval *planula larva*. The planula differs from the *planula* of Hydrozoa in its method of formation and in having a coelenteron and blastopore. These larvae, can be seen on the oral arms of female *Aurelia.*

Planula larva

They become free from the oral arms of the female and after a short free swimming they sink at the bottom of sea. Now planula loses its cilia and the larva is fixed to the substratum by its broad aboral end.

The planula metamorphoses into a small trumpet-shaped polyp or *hydratuba* which has a manubrium and the blastopore opens to become the mouth. Latter, the tentacles are also formed around the mouth, first of all, two *per-radial* tentacles as buds. After sometimes two other *perradial* tentacles are formed longitudinally to the first two are formed and then four *inter-radial* and eight *ad-radial* tentacles arise. The endoderm of coelenteron forms four inter-radial longitudinal ridges called the *gastric ridges* or *mesenteries*. The mouth becomes square and the manubrium forms funnel-like depression called *septal funnel* or *infundibula*. These changes convert the planula into a hydratuba. A stolen arises at the base of hydratuba.

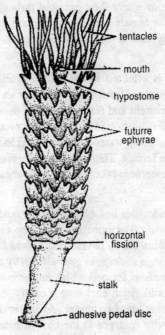

tentacles

mouth

hypostome

futurre ephyrae

horizontal fission

stalk

adhesive pedal disc

Fig. 4.10. *Aurelia*. A strobila.

The hydratuba buds off new hydratubae, from its stolen in summer. These hydratubae may separate after summer. Hydratuba stops budding but each continues to feed and generally passes the winter of the first year and buds other hydratuba. In the next winter the hydratuba undergoes a process of transverse fission, *strobilation*. The dividing hydratuba is called *Scyphistoma* or *Strobila*.

Strobilization of Scyphistoma

In winter and autumn seasons, the body of scyphistoma divides by a series of ring-like transverse constrictions. These constrictions gradually deepen and the body of scyphistoma appears like many saucers placed upside down over each other. The segmented scyphistoma is known as the *strobila* and the process is strobilization and its saucer-like segments as the *ephyrae* or *ephyrulae*.

During the formation of the ephyrae, eight bifid arms, 4 per-radial and 4 inter-radial grow out from the periphery. A rhopalium appears in the terminal notch of each arm. The gastric ridges breakdown, septal funnels disappear due to expansion of the area occupied by them. The enteron sends a branch in each arm. When fully formed, the ephyrae break from scyphistoma. The scyphistoma loses its tentacles before it casts off the first ephyra. Thus the ephyrae are constricted off one by one from the upper surface of scyphistoma. The successive ephyrae released from strobila have no tentacles. While the ephyrae are being detached, their enteron closes on the proximal side but on the distal side remains open and its margin grows out to form a short manubrium with a square mouth its tip. This side becomes subumbrella while proximal becomes exumbrella.

Strobilization is of two types : *Polydisc and monodisc.* In polydisc strobilization several ephyrae are formed. In monodisc strobilization only one ephyra is formed and it takes place during unfavourable conditions.

Sometimes scyphistoma does not undergo strobilization. It gets detached and changes into a single free-swimming ephyra that under goes metamorphosis into a medusa.

Ephyra

The *ephyra* is a young medusoid form showing tetramerous symmetry. Its margins has four per-radial and four inter-radial bifid arms. Each arm is deeply notched distally to form marginal lappets. The groove between them is sensory in nature and has a short tentacle which later becomes tentaculocyst. The larva has a small stomach with gastric filaments (which are derived from mesenteries), a manubrium and a rectangular mouth on the subumbrellar surface. The stomach gives off canals which go into the arms. These canals represent perradial and inter-radial canals. The ad-radial canal appears a little later.

Metamorphosis of ephyra into *Aurelia*

The ephyra swims actively in sea water feeding on minute organisms such as protozoans which are caught by the lappets and passed into the mouth.It grows in size. The mesogloea increases so that the two layers of endoderm together to form an endoderm lamella except the enteron. The ad-radial region grows more rapidly and fills their clefts so that the umbrella becomes circular and saucer-shaped and resembles the adult medusa. Now the four oral arms and numerous marginal tentacles appear so that the ephyra is finally transformed into an adult *Aurelia*.

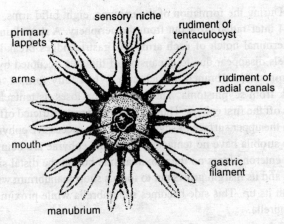

Fig. 4.11. *Aurelia* A free ephyra.

It has been seen that very large eggs of *Aurelia* develop into *actinula larva* which gives rise to ephyrae larvae directly. The small eggs give rise to *planula larvae* which become hydratubae and then scyphistomae which strobilate ephyrae.

Alternation of Generations

The life cycle of *Aurelia* is said to show alteration of generations. The adult medusa represent the sexual phase producing gametes. The zygote produces fixed Scyphistoma (polypoid) which represents the asexual phase resembling the polyp of colony. The scyphistoma reproduces asexually by strobilization to form ephyrae which metamorphose into *adult Aurelia* which is a sexual form.

According to some workers, the development of *Aurelia* does not show true alternation of generations. The adult, *Aurelia* medusa is formed by the metamorphosis of an ephyra larva produced as one of the several transverse segments of the polypoid scyphistoma, whereas in *Obelia* the medusa is developed as a bud on a branched polypoid colony. In *Aurelia* the polypoid phase is greatly reduced in the life-cycle. As the medusa is formed by the metamorphosis of an ephyra and the life cycle is continuous process so that there is no metagenesis or alternation of generation current to new places where they give rise to young anemones.

Comparison between *Obelia* and *Aurelia*

Obelia	Aurelia
Polyp	
1. It is one of the zooids of a polymorphic colony.	1. It is a larval stage in the life history called scyphistoma.
2. The adult is covered with perisarc.	2. Perisarc is absent.
3. It is formed as a bud on the colony.	3. It develops from zygote.
4. Blastostyle directly produces medusa by budding	4. Scyphistoma produces by strobilisation which metamorphose into medusa.
5. There are no gastric ridges or mesenteries so that the enteron is undivided.	5. Body wall projects into enteron as four longitudinal septa, the mesenteries, along inter-radii.
6. It is meant for feeding and defending the colony.	6. It is meant for asexual multiplication.
Medusa	
7. Medusa phase is reduced and known as swimming bells.	7. Medusa phase is dominant and known as jelly fish.
8. It is very small in size measuring 6 mm. in diameter.	8. It is large and measures upto 4 inches or 30 cm.
9. The oral arms are absent.	9. Four oral arms surrounding the mouth.
10. Manubrium is long.	10. It is short.
11. Bell margin is not scalloped.	11. Bell margin is scalloped, having eight notches for tentaculocysts.
12. Bell margin beset with few long solid tentacles.	12. Bell margin beset with many small, hollow tentacles.
13. True velum is present, projects inwards from bell margin and lacks endodermal canals.	13. True velum is absent, inconspicuous velarium present containing endodermal canals.
14. Sense organs are ad-radial in position, lies at the bases of the tentacles, are without protectives lappets and hood. These are purely ectodermal sacs and are called statocysts.	14. Sense organs are per-radial and inter-radial in position, lie in the marginal notches, are protected by lappets and hood, enclose gastrodermal canal and are called rhopalia.
15. Canal system simple, stomach not well defined. Gastric pouches are absent. Canals unbranched.	15. Canal system complicated stomach specious. Gastric pouches are present. Canals are branched.
16. Gastric ridges and filaments absent.	16. Gastric ridges bearing filaments are present.

17. No current of water circulates in the canal system.	17. Water circulates indefinite course in gastrovascular system.
18. Mesogloea non-cellular.	18. Mesogloea contains amoeboid cells and fibres.
19. Muscles strands derived from both ectodermal and endodermal cells.	19. Muscles strands only derived from ectoderm.
20. There is a double nerve-ring in the margin bell.	20. There is no double nerve ring, in the margin of bell. Instead there are 8 separate nerve centres besides the sense organs.
21. Nematocysts confined to the manubrium and tentacles only.	21. Nematocysts are present all over the bell, manubrium, oral arms and gastric filaments.
22. Nematocysts are only one type i.e., penetrant type.	22. Nematocysts are of two types, Atrichous isorphizoas and hetero-trichous microbasic euryteles.
23. Gonads lie on radial canals externally.	23. Gonads lie on the floor of gastric pouches internally.
24. Gametes derived from ectoderm.	24. Gametes derived from endoderm.
25. Subgerminal pits are absent.	25. Subgerminal pits are present below gonads.
26. Gametes are shed in sea water by the rupture of gonads.	26. Gametes are shed in the gastric pouches, from where they escape into the sea water.

Development

27. Fertilization is external.	27. Fertilization is internal.
28. Cleavage is holoblastic equal.	28. Cleavage is holoblastic but unequal.
29. Gastrulation by delamination.	29. Gastrtulation by invagination.
30. Planula larva is without blastopore and coelenteron.	30. Planula larva has blastopore and coelenteron.
31. Planula forms hydrula stage which produces *Obelia* colony by budding.	31. Planula forms trumpet-like scyphistoma which forms ephyrae by strobilization.
32. Life-cycle shows metagenesis.	32. No alteration of generations in life cycle.

Revision Questions

1. Give an account of structure and life-history of *Aurelia*.
2. Give an illustrated account of the life-history of *Aurelia*. Does it exhibit true alternation of generation?

3. Mention the similarities and dissimilarities between *Obelia* and *Aurelia*.

4. Describe the scyphozoan polyp and compare it with that of Sea-anemone.

5. Give an account of structure of gastrovascular system in *Aurelia*.

6. Give an account of the sturcutre of *Aurelia*. How does *Aurelia* differ from the medusa of *Obelia*.

7. Write short notes on : (a) Tentaculocysts, (b) Ephyra, (c) Scyphistoma, (d) Strobilization.

Metridium

Sea-anemones are among the most beautiful and prominent animals of the sea-shore. They are brightly coloured and when fully expanded, turn the sea-floor into a flower-bed. When disturbed these sensitive animals contract to shapeless mass.

SYSTEMATIC POSITION

Phylum	-	Coelenterata
Class	-	Anthozoa
Subclass	-	Hexacorallina
Order	-	Actiniaria
Genus	-	*Metridium*

Habits and habitat

The sea-anemone is a large, sessile, marine polyp. It has a thick columnar body and numerous short tentacles. There is no trace of a medusoid stage in the life-cycle. It occurs commonly on rocks, weeds, shells etc. It occurs from tide pool to a depth of 90 fathoms. It is found from New Jersey as the variety *M. marginatum*. This form also occurs on the coast of Europe. Another species, *M. fimbriatum* extends the range of the Pacific. It is solitary and plankton feeder. It reproduces sexually as well as asexually. Development indirect through a planula larva.

EXTERNAL FEATURES

Shape, Size and Colouration

It has a stout, cylindrical body with a crown of tentacles. It measures 5-7 cm in length. Sea-anemones are often brightly coloured. They may be white, green, blue, orange or red or a combination of many colours.

Divisions of Body

The body is divisible into three parts:

(i) Oral disc

(ii) Column

(iii) Pedal disc.

(i) Oral disc

It is the upper or distal free end of the body. It expands horizontally to form a round saucer-shaped *peristome* or *oral disc*. Many small and hollow tentacles are present along its margin in the form of a crown. These tentacles are arranged in several circles around the slit-like mouth present in the centre of the oral-disc. Generally, the number of tentacles in each circle is in the multiple of six. Their number increases with the age. The tentacles posses nematocysts.

(ii) Column

The upright part of the body is thick walled and called the column. The junction of the oral disc and the column is called the *margin* and it may be marked by a groove. The surface of the column is beset with adhesive warts or pappillae by whose secretions the animal gets the stones, sand and shells attached to its body surface and gets completely hidden from view. The wall of the column may vary from thin transparent to thick leathery condition. The column may be differentiated into an upper short region the *capitulum* and a lower thick walled region, the *scapus*. Scapus just before joining the capitulum stands up as a distinct fold, the *collar* or *parapet*, and a groove called *fosse* results between the collar and base of the capitulum. Irrespective of the presence or absence of the capitulum the upper part of the scapus may be differentiated into a short region, the *scapulus*. Just below the margin or at the lower boundary of capitulum

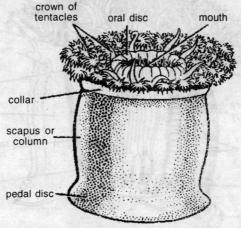

Fig. 5.1. *Metridium*, External view.

there is the marginal *sphincter*. This acts to close the margin or upper end of the scapus over the retracted oral disc or capitulum when sea-anemone contracts. The sea-anemone having parapet, the sphincter is in the wall of the fosse. The wall of the column presents a variety of special structures or protuberances which may be ornamented with adhesive or protective papillae. Thus they cover themselves by sands and stones. These papillae may be arranged in rows. In some of the sea-anemones the column wall is provided with a number of pores, called as *cinclides* through which *acontia* protrude out. They also serve for the expulsion of water when the column contracts.

(iii) Pedal disc

The base is demarcated externally from the column by a groove, the *limbus,* and is expanded to form a circular pedal disc for attachment to the substratum.The animal is not sedentary because it can creep by gliding motion of the basal disc which puts out a turgid lobe in the direction of movement while the opposite end contracs.The speed of its movement is about 8 cm. per hour.

INTERNAL STRUCTURE

The internal structure of a sea-anemone can be studied by cutting it longitudinally, through the mouth, and transversely.

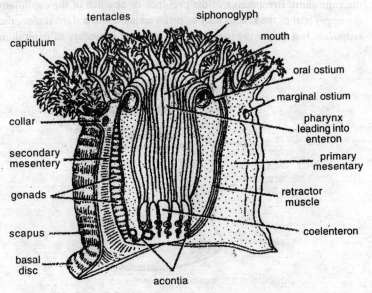

Fig. 5.2. *Metridium.* Vertical longitudinal section to show internal structure.

Enteric cavity or gastro-vascular system

The mouth opens into a muscular, flat, tube-like *gullet or pharynx*. It is formed by the inversion of the wall of the oral disc. Gullet extends downward and opens into the central part of enteron or gastro-vascular cavity. The pharynx or stomodaeum extends to about 2/3 of the length of the body and is lined with ectoderm. The free lower end of stomodaeum is produced at each end of the long diameter into *lappet*. At one end or both the ends of the long diameter of stomodaeum there is a longitudinal ciliated grove, the *siphonoglyph*. Specimens with one and two siphonoglyphs are called *monoglyphic* and *diglyphic* respectively. If there are two siphonoglyphs, the major one is called *sulcus* and the other is *sulculus*. This variation in the number of siphonoglyphs in *Metridium* is probably due to asexual reproduction or regeneration after injury. The presence of siphonoglyph breaks the radial symmetry of the animal and it appears bilateral. This type of symmetry is called *biradial symmetry*. Sometimes specimens are without siphonoglyph or three siphonoglyphs.

The enteron or gastro-vascular cavity is divided into a number of raidally arranged cavity by vertical partitions that extends from the body wall inwards to varying distances. These partitions are called *septa* or *mesenteries* and the cavities between them are *intermesenteries chambers*.

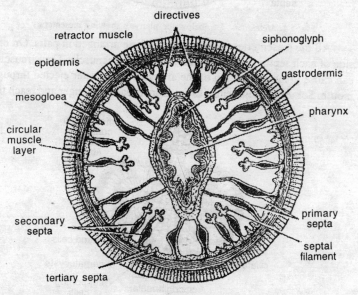

Fig. 5.3. *Metridium* T.S. through pharynx showing mesenteries

The chambers between the mesenteries of some pair are called *endocoels* and the chambers between the adjacent inesenteries are called *exocoels*.

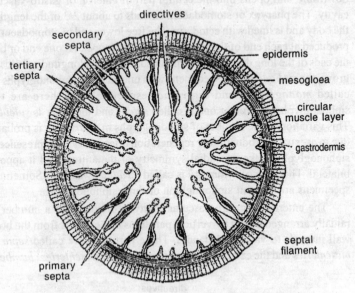

Fig. 5.4. *Metridium*. T.S. below the pharynx showing mesenteries.

All the mesenteries are not equal and are arranged in pairs. On one side of each septum runs a longitudinal retractor muscle. These muscles can cause great contraction of the animal so that water ejected through mouth. Some of the mesenteries are more broad and longer and reach the

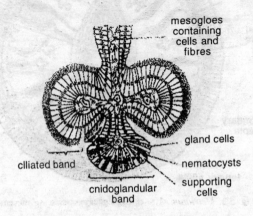

Fig. 5.5. *Metridium* T.S. mesentric filament.

stomodaeum. These are called *primary, complete* or *perfect* mesenteries. There are usually six pairs of primary mesenteries in *Metridium*.

A little short and incomplete *secondary* mesenteries are found in between the pairs of primary mesenteries. More small pairs of *tertiary* mesenteries also found between them. These are attached to the body wall but do not extend up to the stomodaeum. In *Metridium*, the position of siphonoglyph and mesenteries becomes much irregular due to asexual reproduction. The chambers between the primary mesenteries are in open communication with each other only below the stomodaeum. In stomodaeum, the adjacent chambers communicate with each other only by one or two apertures, called *ostia*. The ostia found on the outer side of the mesenteries are called *marginal ostia*, while those found on the gullet side are known as *oral ostia*. In secondary mesenteries only marginal ostia are found. The cavities of the tentacles also open into intermesenteric chambers.

Each mesentery has two layers of endoderm. Mesogloea is present between these two layers. These increase surface area for digestion.

Below the gullet, the primary mesenteries curve away from the centre and towards the base all mesenteries curve towards the centre, reaching various points on the base. The free-edges of the mesenteries are thickened to form *mesenteric filaments*. These are trifid in the region of gullet. The lower part of each mesenteric filament is in the form of a free fine thread called *acontium*. The acontia can be protruded through the special apertures called *cinclide* present on the body wall or through the mouth. Nematocysts and gland cells are also found in acontia.

Histology

The body wall consists of the usual two layers, *epidermis* and *gastrodermis* with an intermediate layer of mesogloea.

(i) Epidermis

It is made up of *columnar supporting cells* containing between them slender *sensory cells*, mucous secreting *gland cells* and *cnidoblasts*. The supporting cells are ciliated on the tentacles and oral disc. The sensory cells are numerous in the tentacles, oral disc and stomodaeum but they decrease in the column and again abundant in the basal disc.

(ii) Gastrodermis

It is made up of *epithelio-muscular cells* in which the bases of cells are drawn out into the muscle fibres, these muscle fibres are circular in tentacles, oral disc, column and basal disc. On the mesenteries they form strong retractor muscles which run longitudinally. Between the epithelio-

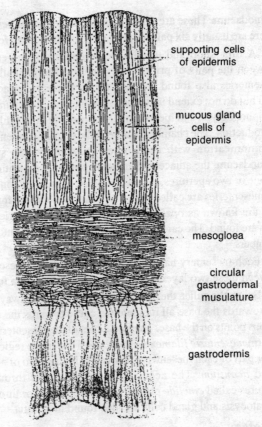

supporting cells
of epidermis

mucous gland
cells of
epidermis

mesogloea

circular
gastrodermal
musulature

gastrodermis

Fig. 5.6. *Metridium*. Transverse section.

muscular cells are granular, *gland cells* which secrete enzymes.*Sensory cells* and *nematocyst* on mesenteries are also found. The cnidoblasts and gland cells are confined to the middle lobe of the trilobed mesenteric filaments. These lobes are, therefore, known as *cnido-glandular bands*. The lateral lobes bear cilia, hence called *ciliated bands*.

(iii) Mesogloea

It is the intermediate layer, thick and tough. It has the form of connective tissue. It consists of matrix with amoebocytes and abundant fibres.

Nematocysts

Metridium has four types of nematocysts. These are usually slightly curved and without a cnidocil.

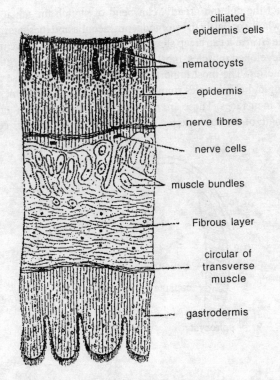

Fig. 5 7. *Metridium.* T.S. of tentacle.

(i) *Spirocystis*. The spirocysts has a thin single-walled capsule and spirally coiled, unarmed tube or thread of uniform size. The capsule contains mucoprotein or glycoprotein. These are found on oral disc and tentacles.

(ii) *Basitrichous isorhizas*. It has oval capsule containing a mixture of phenol and proteins. The thread or tube is of uniform size and armed with spines. It remains open at the tip. The butt is absent.

(iii) *Microbasic mastigophores*. It has rounded capsule, the butt is long and bears spines in a spiral. The thread is long and closed at the tip.

(iv) *Microbasic amastigophores*. It has an oval capsule with a short butt armed with spines in a spiral. Thread is absent.

The last three nematocysts are found everywhere on the body.

Arrangement of muscles

It will be seen from the general account of the anemone given above that it has a structure of a large and elaborate polyp. Due to its complicated structure, it can perform various kinds of movements. It can expand or contract the column greatly, can bend or stretch the tentacles and can evert wholly or partly the stomodaeum, acontia and mesenteries. Besides, like the *Hydra*, it can creep slowly on its base. All these movements require well developed muscles, most of which are found in connection with the mesenteries. The most important and conspicuous of these muscles are the longitudinal muscles running the entire length of the mesenteries on one of their faces. These are *retractor muscles* and when they contract, the length of the mesenteries, as well as the body itself, is considerably

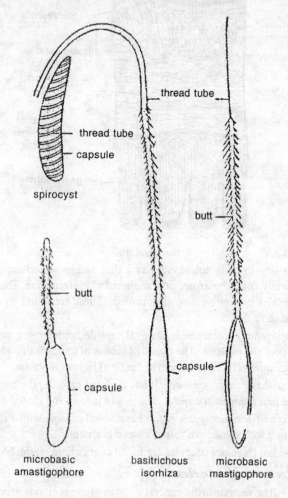

Fig. 5.8. *Metridium*. Types of nematocysts.

reduced. These also cause the contraction of the tentacles. Another set of muscles passes obliquely across the upper and lower inner angles. These are *parietal muscles* and by their contraction the column is drawn towards the base. A third set of mesenteric muscles consists of *transverse muscles* and runs at right angle to the longitudinal muscles. These are comparatively weak and oppose the action of the longitudinal muscles and reduce the diameter of the animal to some extent. There are also circular fibres making a sphincter at the junction of the column and oral disc which help to retract the oral disc and the tentacles by their contraction. Besides, these, muscles are present in the tentacles, gullet, etc. It has been stated that the longitudinal muscles stretch on a particular face of the mesentery. The oblique muscles also run on the same face, but their arrangement on the different mesenteries is not arbitrary. On the other hand, they have a regular arrangement which, along with the compressed nature of the gullet and the presence of the siphonoglyphs imparts a distinct bilateral symmetry to the animal.

The mesenteries are always present in pairs and the pairs of mesenteries corresponding to the siphonoglyphs are called *directive mesenteries*. In the directive mesenteries, the muscles face away from each other. In the other pairs of mesenteries, whether primary, secondary or tertiary, the muscles face towards each other.

PHYSIOLOGY

Movements

They are inactive animals but due to development of musculature they show following movements:

(i) The column can be expanded or retracted.

(ii) Tentacles extend to a considerable length or may be completely retracted back and become hidden by the upper end of the column in which becomes folded over them.

(iii) Stomodaeum and septa may be partially everted through the mouth.

(iv) It can slowly glide on the substratum and by slow creeping movements can change its position. This is brought about by muscular undulations of pedal disc. The movement is very slow about 8 cm/hr.

Nutrition

The animal is quite voracious, and feeds on molluscs, crustaceans, worms, sea-urchins and fishes, etc. The prey is captured and partly paralysed, before ingestion, by the nematocystst of tentacles, oral disc and acontia. Mouth opens and the gullet protrudes out as small lobe. The part of the oral disc between the food and the mouth contracts so that the lobes of the gullet reach the food and grasp it.

Most of the smaller sea-anemones are ciliary feeders. Cilia on the outer surface of the column beat towards the oral disc, where ciliary currents sweep the food particles to the tips of tentacles. The latter bend down to transfer the food into the mouth. Mucous and nematocysts play an important role in capture of the planktonic organisms. The captured food is swept down the stomodaeum into the gastrovascular cavity.

In the gastrovascular cavity the prey is killed, if still alive, by nematocysts and is subjected to *intercellular digestion*. The latter reduces the food to pieces under the action of a protease of the nature of trypsin secreted by the gland cells of the cnido-glandular bands of the mesenteries. The pieces are then engulfed by the gastrodermal cells, except those of the cnido-glandular bands, for *intracellular digestion*. The latter is brought about by proteases of the nature of pepsin and erepsin and lipases. Carbohydrates are perhaps not utilized by the sea-anemone.

The digested food is absorbed in the gastrodermis while the undigested food is ejected out through the mouth.

The excess food is stored in the gastrodermis chiefly as fat. The sea-anemone can live without food for a long time, utilizing its reserve fat.

Respiration and Excretion

Respiration is aerobic. Epidermis and gastrodermis are in contact with water. With the result, oxygen of the water easily diffuse into the cells and the carbon dioxide of the cells diffuses into the water. Definite respiratory currents are maintained to renew water in the enteron. The cilia of the siphonoglyphs beat inwards and those of the rest of the gullet beat outwards. This makes the water current enter through the siphonoglyphs and leave through the gullet. Water inside the enteron is circulated by gastrodermal cilia. Ammonia is the chief nitrogenous waste product. It is diffused out in the surrounding water.

Nervous System

Specific sense organs do not occur in anemones. The nervous system is very simple, basically similar to that of other coelenterates, and is *synaptic*. It is represented by a typical diffuse *nerve-net* with no indication of a centralized nervous control, as in medusae. It consists of an *epidermal plexus*, between the epithelium and muscular layer, and a *gastrodermal plexus*, at least in the septa; the two are connected through the mesogloea. Each plexus consists of delicate nerve fibres and large *ganglion cells* occurring chiefly in the tentacles oral disc and pharynx. The reflex behaviour is poor due to lac of a centralized nervous system.

REPRODUCTION

Metridium reproduces both asexually as well as sexually.

I. Asexual Reproduction

It takes place by following methods :

(a) Pedal Laceration

Pedal laceration is the predominant mode of asexual multiplication. In this process, parts of the pedal disc may firmly adhere to the substratum and get torn off as the anemone creeps along. These pieces in a few days develop into small new anemones at the old site and the parent completes its pedal disc at a new place. Or, alternatively, small lobes arise from the margin of the pedal disc and get constricted off. These are carried by water current to new places where they give rise to young anemones.

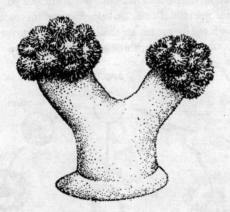

Fig. 5.9. *Metridium* showing longitudinal binary fission.

(b) Longitudinal Binary Fission

The pedal disc elongates in the sagittal plane till it ruptures along the transverse plane. The cut then rapidly extends upwards through the column and the oral disc.

(c) Budding

It involves formation of outgrowths from the column or pedal disc and their mouth transformation into new individuals. The latter ultimately detach from the parent and establish themselves at new places. Budding is of rare occurrence.

Fig. 5.10. *Metridium* showing budding.

II. Sexual reproduction and life cycle

Sea-anemones are dioecious or unisexual. Near the edges of the septa or mesenteries and lying parallel to them, gonads are located. The sex cells are gastrodermal interstitial cells that ripen in the mesogloea. Eggs or spermatozoa produced by gonads are discharged into gastrovascular cavity and finally pass out in sea water through mouth. Fertilization is external

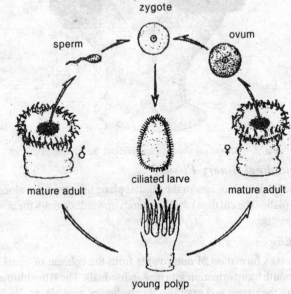

Fig. 5.11. *Metridium* Life-history.

and takes place in sea water. Zygote develops after undergoing total, unequal or equal cleavage in a *coeloblastula*. The endoderm is formed by invagination. The embryo elongates into a ciliated planula having in some forms an aboral large hard tuft of cilia. At the oral (posterior) pole the blastopore persists in cases of invagination or soon breaks through. Then blastopore becomes the lower opening of stomodaeum. The planula larva swims for some time and feeds on micro-organisms. Finally it settles down at the bottom of the sea and attaches itself by aboral end. The tentacles, septa and mesogloca are formed and the planula larva changes into a minute animal.

Regeneration

Metridium has a power of regeneration. If the column is cut across, the aboral part regenerates a new oral disc but the oral part fails to develop a pedal disc. In some cases, instead of a new pedal disc, the oral part regenerates a second set of tentacles at its lower aboral surface. Thus it exhibits a case of *hetermorphosis* or reversed polarity.

Difrerences between Hydrozoan polyp and a Sea-anemone

Hydrozoan Polyp (Hydra)	Sea-anemone
1. Fresh water.	1. Marine.
2. Body long, slender and delicate.	2. Body large, heavier and firm.
3. Mouth circular and at the tip of a conical manubrium	3. Oral cone is absent and mouth is slit-like at the centre of a horizontal disc.
4. Tentacles less, long, arranged in a ring, at the base of manubrium.	4. Tentacles numerous, short usually arranged in multiple of six, on the oral disc.
5. Column without pore.	5. Column with numerous pores, the *cinclides*
6. Mouth directly leads into the gastro-vascular cavity.	6. Mouth leads into a long flattened gullet or stomodaeum lined by ectoderm.
7. Gastrovascular cavity specious, undivided.	7. Gastrovascular cavity is divided into a number of chambers by mesenteries.
8. Mesogloca is thin and without any cell.	8. Mesogloca with fibres and amoebocytes in a gelatinous matrix.

9. Nematocysts are four types: penetrants, volvents, holotrichous isorhizas and atrichous isorhizas. They posses operculum and cnidocil.

9. Nematocysts are four types: spirocysts, basitrichous isorhizas, microbasic mastigophores and microbasic amastigophores. Operculum and cnidocil are absent.

10. Musculature less developed.

10. Musculature well developed.

11. Asexual reproduction by budding only.

11. Asexual reproduction by pedal laceration, budding and longitudinal fission.

12. Gonad develop externally are ectodermal in origin.

12. Gonad develop internally on mesenteries are gastrodermal in origin.

13. Gastrulation by multiple ingression followed by delamination.

13. Gastrulation by invagination.

14. Resting cysts are formed during unfavourable conditions. Dispersal by these cysts.

14. No cyst formation.

15. Planula larva is absent.

15. Planula larva is present and dispersal by these larvae.

Revision Questions

1. Give an account of external and internal structure of *Metridium*.
2. Compare the polyps of *Metridium* and *Obelia.*
3. Draw a well-labelled diagram of longitudinal section of *Metridium*.
4. Give an account of the physiology and life-history of *Metridium*.
5. Write short notes on : (a) Mesenteries, (b) Siphonoglyph, (c) Asexual reproduction of *Metridium*.

6

Mesenteries in Anthozoa

Anthozoans are the coelenterates belonging to the class - Anthozoa. In Anthozoa only the polyps are seen, medusa stage is absent. The polyps have mouth, pharynx gullet or stomodaeum. The stomodaeum hangs into the gastrovascular cavity. The gastrovascular cavity is divided into chambers by mesenteries. The mesenteries are defined as the radiating partitions that extend from the body wall and the stomodaeum. Usually these are present in pairs.

Structure

Mesenteries are more or less evenly spaced around the circumference. The upper margin of each mesentery is attached to the oral disc,the lower margin to the pedal disc and the outer margin to the wall of column. The free- edges of the mesenteries are thickened to from twisted cords, the *mesenteric filaments*. The filaments are trifid in the region of gullet but below gullet they are simple in sub- class Zoantharia. The middle lobe is called *cnido- glandular band*, it contains cnidoblasts and gland cells. The lateral lobes bear cilia and are called *ciliated bands*. The lower ends of mesenteic filaments are produced into free threads, the *acontia*. These are beset with thread cells. These are organs of defence. They can be protruded through the mouth or through the *cinclides* (these are special cells of body wall).

Intermesenteric chambers between the mesenteries of same pair are called *endocoels*,where as chambers present between the mesenteries of the adjacent pairs are termed the *exocoels*. The chambers are separate in the pharyngeal region but they open into the central part of gastrovascular cavity, The mesenteries bear their upper or oral side apertures called *ostia*. Two such ostia are found on each mesentery, the *oral ostium* lies near the body wall. The stomata put the adjacent intermesenteric chambers in communication with one another to permit flow of water between them.

Gonads are located along the inner free edges of the mesenteries just behind the filaments.

Histology

A mesentery consists of a middle supporting lamina of mesogloea covered on both the sides with a layer of gastrodermal cells. The gastrodermis is composed of long columnar supporting cells with sensory cells, enzyme secreting gland cells and nematocysts. Nematocysts are present only in cnidoglandular band. The mesenteries are highly contractile due to presence of three types of muscles: the *longitudinal* or *retractor muscles* which runs as a narrow band from the base of oral disc, the *parietal muscles* that runs obliquely across the lower outer angle; and *transverse muscles* which run parallel to the oral disc. The longitudinal and parietal muscles are so thick so as to form a bulging on one side of mesentery. This bulging is called *exocoelic*. Here the bulging face away from each other. If the bulging face one another it is called *endocoelic*.

The muscles form the chief means of contraction and extension of the body.

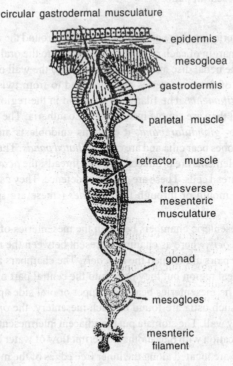

circular gastrodermal musculature

— epidermis

— mesogloea

— gastrodermis

— parietal muscle

— retractor muscle

— transverse mesenteric musculature

— gonad

— mesogloes

— mesnteric filament

Fig. 6.1. *Metridium*. T.S. mesentery.

TYPICAL TYPE OF MESENTERIES

The typical type of mesenteries are present in *Metridium*. Six pairs of more broad niesenteries extending from the body wall to the gullet. These are called *primary mesenteries*. A little short and incomplete *secondary mesenteries* are found in between the pairs of primary mesenteries. More small pairs of *tertiary mesenteries* are also found between them. The secondary and tertiary mesenteries are attached to the body wall but they do not extend upto gullet.

TYPES OF MESENTERIES

Based on the position and its development, the mesenteries are groups into, following:

1. Complete and incomplete mesenteries

The complete mesenteries are those connecting the body wall and stomodaeum *e.g.* Primary mesenteries. The incomplete mesenteries are those extending midway between the body wall and the stomodaeum *e.g.* secondary and tertiary mesenteries.

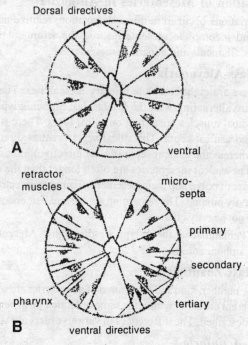

Fig. 6.2. T.S. through pharynx A *Gonactinia*, B *Protanthea*.

2. Couples and pairs

The couples refer to all the mesenteries which occur in one half and similar to the other half. Whereas on either side of the animal, the mesenteries facing. each other in two's are called *pairs*.

3. Macrosepta and microsepta

The large sized septa are called *macrosepta e.g.* primary mesenteries. The small-sized septa are called *microsepta e.g.* tertiary mesenteries.

4. Directives

The pharynx commonly bears a ciliated groove, the *siphonoglyph*. The septa that are connected to the siphonoglyph are called *directives*.

5. Sulcal and asulcal mesenteries

If two siphonoglyphs are present, the main siphonoglyph is called *sulcus* and the directives connected to it are called *sulcal*. The secondary siphonoglyph is called *sulculus* and the directives connected to it are called *asulcal*.

Disposition of Mesenteries in Anthozoa

Variations occur in number, disposition, relative numbers of complete and incomplete mesenteries and the arrangements of retractor muscles, filaments and gonads in mesenteries.

Sub-class-Alcyonaria

There are eight complete primary mesenteries. They are unpaired. These are alternating with the 8 tentacles. Siphonoglyph is single. The longitudinal muscles are strong on sulcal faces. There is a pair of sulcal septa and asulcal septa. The sulcal septa (ventral directive) face each other whereas the asulcal septa (dorsal directive) look away from each other. The asulcal mesenteries are often longer than the others, continue to the base of polyp and their mesenteric filaments are ectodermal in origin and heavily ciliated. The remaining six are smaller, endodermal in origin and are not heavily ciliated.

In Pennatulacea, the polyps are dimorphic. Mesenteries are found only in siphonozooids.

Sub-class-Zoantharia

The number, kind and disposition of mesenteries are so variable among the different orders or within the same order that no generalised condition can be described. The differences in various orders are summarized :

Order-Actiniaria

In *Edwardsia* there are eight macrosepta. But there are only four

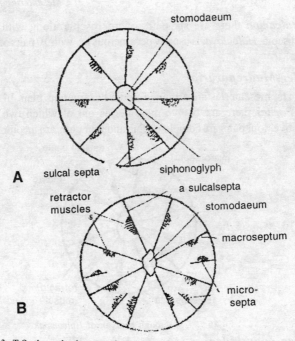

Fig. 6.3. T.S. through pharyngeal region. A—*Alcyonium*, B—*Edwardsia*.

microsepta facing the salcus. The sulcal retractors face away. Besides four microsepta are also found near the oral disc, pairing with single microsepta in such a manner that their retractors face each other. In *Gonactinia*, in the exocoels, between these six of mesenteries, are usually present additional two pairs of microsepta. There are six pairs of microsepta in *Protanthea*. *Halcampoides* shows a similar condition in mesenteries as in sea-anemone.

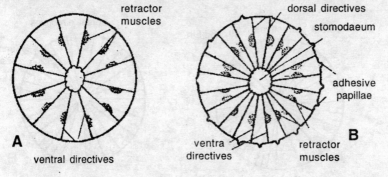

Fig. 6.4. T.S. through pharynx. A—*Halcampoides*, B—*Haloclava*.

In *Halcampa* there are six pairs of microsepta along with six pairs microsepta. *Haloclava*, is usually decamerous i.e. with 10 pairs of complete septa.

Order-Madreporaria

The mesenteries are arranged in the hexamerous plan. In *Acropora* and *Porites* there are twelve mesenteries out of which two pairs are directive, four pairs are complete septa and four pairs are incomplete septa.

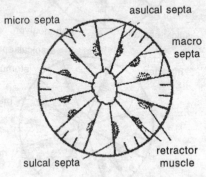

Fig. 6.5. T.S. through pharynx of *Halcampa*.

Order-Zoanthidea

The number of mesenteries is six or multiple of six. The arrangement is different from any living Anthozoa but some- what resembles that of extinct Tetracoralla. The mesenteries are paired and the arrangement of septa is called *brachyncemous* in *Zoanthus*. This includes one pair of macrosepta, one pair of microsepta and one pair of ventral directives. Some zoanthids like *Epizoanthus*, however, shows the macrocnemous arrangement. This

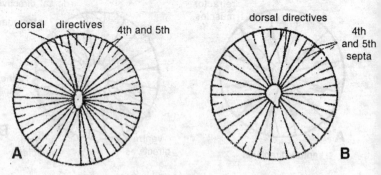

Fig. 6.6. T.S. through A—*Zoanthus*, B—*Epizoanthus*.

includes threepairs of macrosepta, the ventral directives and the fourth and fifth septa on each side counting from the dorsal directives.

Order-Antipatharia

There are ten complete mesenteries, arranged in couples, but there may be six or twelve. Of these six are primary mesenteries including four directives and two transverse. The transverse are largest and bear gonads and filaments. The septal muscle is poorly developed.

Order-Ceriantharia

The septal arrangement is quite different from that of other anthozoans. *Cerianthus* shows numerous, complete but coupled mesenteries. The number is not definite. During growth new mesenteries added continuously. The ventral directives are very small. The retractor muscles are absent. Three most dorsal couples, including the directives and two couples to either side of them develop first in the embryo hence called *protosepta* and the rest-too short to extend ventrally are called *metasepta*.

7

Nematocysts

These are diagnostic of coelenterates for defense and offense. They develop in special cells called *nematoblasts*, or *cnidocytes*. They are also known as stinging cells or nettle cells. Actually these are not cells but cell-organoids and are made up of a substance similar of chitin.

Distribution

Nematocysts are located all over the body except on the basal disc or pedal disc. These are lodged between or invaginated within epithelio-muscular cells. They are specially abundant on the tentacles. Here they are arranged in groups. These groups are called *batteries*. A battery may consists of one or two large nematocysts surrounded by cysts, each, in its own cnidocyte.

Size

Nemetocysts are minute structures. The capsule measures 5-50μ in length. The tube is several mm. in length.

Structure

A cnidocyte is a rounded or oval cell with a basal nucleus. One end of the cell contains a short, stiff, bristle called *cnidocil* in hydrozoans and scyphozoans. The cnidocil has an ultrastructure similar to that of a flagellum which is exposed to the surface. A cnidocil is usually absent in anthozoans. The interior of the cell is filled with nematocyst. The nematocyst consists of a rounded, oval pyriform or elongated soluble-walled *capsule* containing a coiled, usually *pleated tube*. The base of the tube or thread may be swollen into a *butt*. The tube on its outer surface has three spiral ridges, each bearing a row of spines. The spines may be present throughout the tube or only on a part of it. The end of the capsule that is directed toward the outside is covered by a lid or *operculum*. The capsule is full of a poisonous fluid, the *hypnotoxin* which contains proteins and about 75% as virulent as cobra venom. In hydrozoans and scyphozoans, *support rods* run the length of cnidocyte, and the base is anchored to the lateral extensions of an epitheliomuscular cell. The base of the cnidocyte may also be associated with a neuron terminal.

Discharge of Nematocyst

In an undischarged nematocyst, the butt lie invested in the capsule with the spines on its inner surface and the tube coiled round it. The discharge mechanism apparently involves a change in the permeability, of the capsule wall. Under the combined influence of mechanical and chemical stimuli, which are initially received and conducted by the cnidocil, the operculum (hydrozoans and scyphozoans) or apical flap (anthozoans) of cnida opens. Hydrostatic pressure within the capsule everts the tube and the entire nematocyst explodes to the outside. Discharge can apparently be affected by nerve impulses from the associated neuron terminal, and perhaps neuronal connections serve to bring about coordinated firing by a large number of nematocysts.

Nematocyst may be used but once and are released from the cnidocyte after discharge. New cnidocytes are formed from nearby interstitial cells. Studies on *Hydra littorals* (*Kline,* 1961) indicates that about 25% of nematocysts in the tentacles are lost in the process of eating. These discharged nematocysts are replaced within 48 hours.

Development

These are developed from the interstitial cells of the region away from the region where they function. The process of their formation is not well understood. A cnidocyte develops a vacuole in which a single walled capsule is secreted. Later on the outer wall is formed around it. Inside the capsule appears an elongated body that differentiates into the thread tube. The young cnidocyte (containing developing nematocyst) migrates to its final position through the gastro-vascular cavity. For this purpose, the cnidocyte passes through the mesogloea into the gastrodermal cells. which then transfer it into the gastrovacular cavity as such enclosed in a mass of gasrodermal cytoplasm. Alternatively a gastrodermal cell with a young nematocyst may become free and move in an amoeboid manner in the gastrovasular cavity. From gastrovascular cavity the cnidocyte is ingested by the gastrodermal cells which transfer it once again into the epidermis. Here it completes its differentiation.

Types of Nematocysts

Weill (1964) described seventeen different types of nematocysts based on the diagnostic characters of the tube or thead. He studied about 119 species of different coelenterates. Recent classification has been suggested by *Weill* (1964), *Werner* (1965), *Deroux* (1966) and *Mariscal* (1972); I *Astomocnidae*. Tube closed at the distal end.

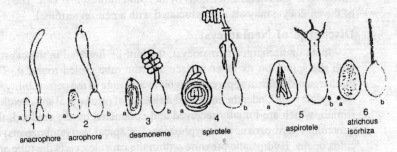

Fig. 7.1. Various types of nematocysts (a)—Undischarged (b)—Discharged.

A. Rhopalonemses. Tube club-shaped and much greater in volume then the capsule.

1. *Anacrophores.* Tube without an apical projection.

2. *Acrophores.* Tube with an apical projection.

B. Spironemes. Thread not club-shaped usually forming a spiral coil distally.

1. *Haplonemes.* Thread without a well-defined shaft.

    (a) *Desmonemes.* Thread-tube coiled like a cork-screw.

2. *Heteronemes.* Thread with a well-defined shift.

    (a) *Rhopaloides.* Shaft of unequal diameter.

3. *Euryteles.* Butt swollen at the distal end.

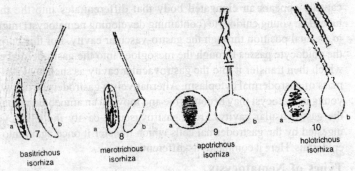

Fig. 7.2. Various types of nematocysts (a)—Undischarged (b)—Discharged.

(a) *Microbasic.* Thread lacking beyond butt, which is less then three times the capsule length.

(I) *Spiroteles.* Thread forms a special coil distally, three spines strongly developed.

(II) *Aspiroteles*. No thread beyond the shaft, three spines strongly developed.

(III) *Stomocnidae*. Thread opens at distal end

A. Haplonemes. Thread without a well-defined shaft.

1. *Isorhizas*. Thread of the same diameter throughout (glutinants).

   (a) *Atrichous*. Thread without well-developed spines only at the base.

   (b) *Basitrichous*. Thread with well-developed spines only at the base.

   (c) *Merotrichous*. Thread with well developed spines on the intermediate part only.

   (d) *Apotrichous*. Thread with developed spines on distal part only.

   (e) *Holotrichous*. Thread with well-developed spines along whole length.

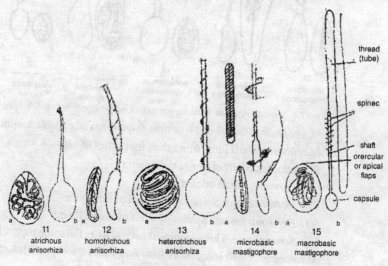

	11	12	13	14	15
	atrichous anisorhiza	homotrichous anisorhiza	heterotrichous anisorhiza	microbasic mastigophore	macrobasic mastigophore

Fig. 7.3. Various types of nematocysts (a)—Undischarged (b)—Discharged.

2. *Anisorhizas*. Thread slightly dilated towards the base

   (a) *Atrchous*. Thread with well developed spines.

   (b) *Homotrichous*. Thread spiny throughout; spines all of equal size.

   (c) *Heterotrichous*. Thread spiny throughout; spines larger at the base of thread.

3. *Heteronemes*. Thread with well defined shaft.

I. *Rhobdoides*. Shaft cylindrical; same diameter throughout.

   (a) *Mastigophores*. Thread continuous beyond the shaft.

(1) *Microbasic*. Shaft short, less then three times of capsule length.

   (a) *Microbasic b-mastigophore*. Shaft tapers slowly into thread.

   (b) *Microbasic p-mastigophore*. Shaft tapers abruptly into thread.

(2) *Macrobasic*. Shaft long more than four times of capsule length.

   (b) *Amastigophores*. Thread absent beyond the shaft.

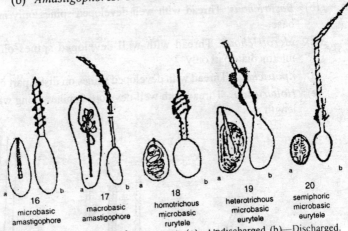

Fig. 7.4. Various types of nematocysts (a)—Undischarged (b)—Discharged.

1. *Macrobasic*. Shaft short, less than three times of capsule length.
2. *Microbasic*. Shaft long, more than four times of capsule length.
3. *Rhopaloides*. Shaft of unequal diameter.
   (a) *Euryteles*. Shaft dilated distally.
   (b) *Homotrichous*. Spines of shaft all of same size
   (c) *Heteroutrichous*. Spines of shaft of unequal size.
   (d) *Semiophoric*. Thread whip-like with larger flat spine medially.
2. *Macrobasic*. Shaft long, more than four times the capsule length.
   (a) *Teletrichous*. Spines only on distal part of shaft.
   (b) *Merotrichous*. Spines not distally only on shaft area of uniform diameter proximal to terminal swelling.
   (c) *Holotrichous*. Shaft spiny along whole length.
   (d) *Stenotales*. Shaft enlarged at base, 3 spines strongly developed.
   ***Birhoploides*.** Shaft of unequal diameter at distal and proximal end.
   ***Spirocysts*.** They have a thin capsule containing a thin long spirally coiled thread without spines.

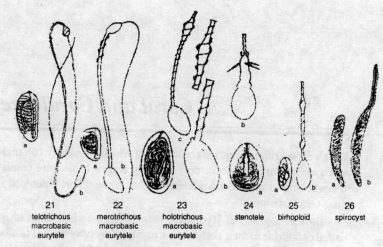

Fig. 7.5. Various types of nematocysts (a)—Undischarged (b)—Discharged.

Function of nematocysts. Different functions are performed by different nematocysts. Rhopalonemes and desmonemes serve for holding the prey. Atrichous isorhozas are adhesive. Function of holotrichous isorhizas is not yet clear. A few nematocysts like stenoteles mastigophores etc. penetrate and anochor in the tissue of prey.

Nature of the discharged fluid is not well-known. The discharge causes paralysing action on the prey and cause burning sensation in the human skin in same cases.

8

Coral and Coral Reefs

Corals are a group of marine coelenterates which are mostly colonial but some are solitary and occur only in polyp stages. Most (ture corals) of them belong to the order Madreporaria but some others belong to sub-class Octocorallia.

Besides a group of Hydrozoa, the *Millipora* and its allies also are called corals due to their skeletal structure but they have no real similarity with ture corals. Since the true corals are the builders of coral reefs and island so only the Madreporarian corals are considered here.

Definition of Coral Reef

Vaughan (1917) has defined a coral reef, "A coral reef is a ridge or mound of limestone, the upper surface of which is near the surface of the sea and which is formed of calcium carbonate by the action of organisms chiefly corals". *Bayer* and *Owre* (1969) mention, "The uppermost layer is a living stratum composed of growing corals, alcyonarians and millepores,

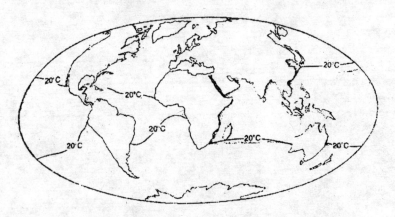

Fig. 8.1. Distribution of coral reefs today (heavy shading).

156

together with a virtually endless array of other organisms that live on or in this frame work, some acting to break down the coral skeletons, others serving to cement the resulting debris together into a conglomerated mass that can act as a foundation for further coral growth. Boring sponges, molluscs, worms and brancles permeate the coral substance and open it to erosional forces that weaken it until it crumbles. Algae, sponges, hydroids, tunicates and other organisms, as well as chemical process, consolidate the fragments and provide a platform for new growth."

Requirements and Distribution

The reef-building corals require warm, clear, shallow water. Therefore, they are confined to continental and island shores in tropical regions (latitude 28° N - 28°S). They flourish best at temperature between 22°C-28°C. As temperature falls with an increase in the depth of sea water, the reef building corals occur up to a depth of 30 metres, or at the most 50 metres. They inhabit water subject to strong wave action, because they

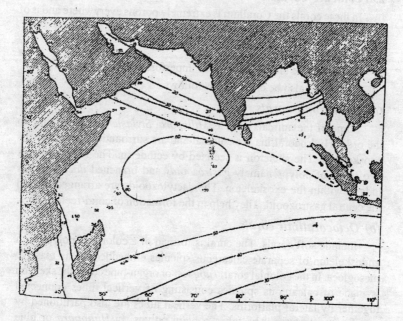

Fig. 8.2. Diversity of corals in the Indian Ocean. Countour lines indicate predicted numbers of genera based on actual collection. The numbers decline with increasing latitude and lower water temperatures. Latitude and long. are given in vertical and horizontal margins.

cannot remove large amounts of sediment likely to accumulate on them in quiet waters. Excessive rains and fresh water are harmful for corals.

The reef building corals are found in two general regions : (i) the *Caribbean waters* including Florida, Bermuda, the Bhamas, and the West Indies; and (ii) the Indo-Pacific water from the east coast of Africa through the Indian Ocean and the Western Pacific as for as Hawaii. The second region specially abounds in coral reefs, and in fact the Pacific north-east of Australia is known as the coral sea.

CLASSIFICATION OF CORALS

The Madriporarian corals are divided into three groups :

1. Imperforate or Aporous corals

They have a complete theca, compact sclerosepta and partitioned into loculae e.g., Astraeid corals, *Favia, Flebellum,*(=*Meandrina,* brain corals).

2. Perforate corals

In these corals the Corallum is extremely porous everywhere and is of loose construction e.g. *Porites, Acropora* (= *Madrepora*), *Montipora.*

3. Fungid corals

These may be either perforate or imperforate e.g., *Fungia*

Corals can also be classified as follows :

(a) Hydrozoan corals

Some of the animals such as *Millepora, Stylaster etc.* belonging to the order Hydrocorallina are colonial and are surrounded by calcareous exoskeleton. The skeleton is secreted by ectoderm. The individual has two types of polyps namely *gastrozooids* and branched *dactylozooids* lodged within the exoskeleton. The dactylozooids are arranged around the central gastrozooid. They help in the formation of coral-reefs.

(b) Octocorallian corals

Include soft corals. The coral is formed of a colony of polyps with endoskeleton of separate calcareous spicules embedded in the massive mesogloea. In the colonial coral, *Tubiproa* or organ-pipe coral, the skeleton is made of calcareous spicules consisting of vertical tubes connected together by lateral platforms. The vertical tubes are also partitioned by smaller cross plates. The tubes contain polyps. In *Haliopora* or blue coral, the calcareous spicules form a massive skeleton of corallium. In *Gorgonia* or sea fan, the colony branches in one plane and the axial skeleton is made up of horny material intermixed with calcareous spicules arranged around the polyps.

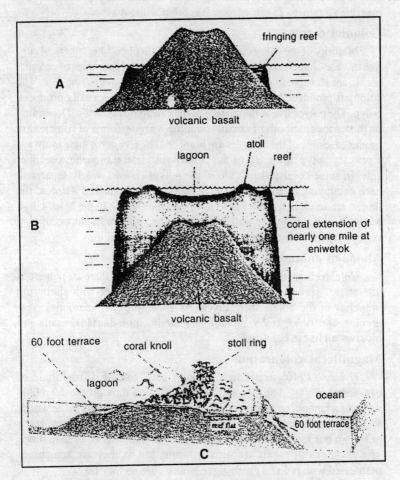

Fig. 8.3. Formation of an Atoll. A, Fringing reef around an emergent volcano. B, Cont. deposition of coral as volcanic cone subsides leads to the formation of a great coralline cap; emergent part of cap is atoll. C; Section through part of atoll.

(c) Hexacorallian corals

These constitute the *stony corals* or *true corals,* They may be solitary or colonial and assume a great variety of forms. They are the main constituents of coral reefs.

Solitary corals

Fungia, Flabellum, Caryophylla, etc., are the solitary corals or cup corals. The corallite is disc-like, cup-like or mushroom shaped in form and measures 5 mm. to 25 cm. across. It is often without a theca.

Colonial corals

Majority of the stony corals is colonial with plate-like, spherical cup-like or vase-shaped skeleton (corallium) The typical examples of colonial corals are *Acropora, Oculina, Favia, Madrepora, Meandrina,* etc. The colony is produced by asexual methods from a single sexually produced polyp. The polyps live at the surface of the calcareous skeleton. Depending on the various methods of asexual budding, varying forms of colonies are produced. Some of the colonies are branched. In *Acropora*, there is always a primary polyp at the top of the colony with lateral branches on either side. In some corals, like *Oculina,* the polyps remain widely separated, each occupying a separate theca. In others, like *Favia* and *Astraea,* the thecae are so close together as to have common walls. In the brain-coral, *Meandrina,* the polyps as well as the thecae become confluent, occupying valleys separated by ridges, on the surface of the corallium.

Abode of animals

Coral reefs are the abode of several other animals as there are numerous interstices, cervices and other hiding places together with sheltering branches of the corals themselves. As such sponges, anemones, sea-urchins, starfishes, crabs, tubicolous-annelids, holothurians, snails and bivalves all live in coral reefs.

Magnificent colouration

Hyman (1940) writes that as coral beds consist of multitude of organisms of varied shapes and colours, viewed through the deep blue water of a lagoon, constitute one of the most beautiful sights in the world, excel the most splendid flower gardens. The coral polyps are yellow, green or brown due to zooxanthellae, but almost any hue can be seen in them. The skeletons of corals are usually white, but as they are sometimes permeated with red and green algae whose colours they take.

CORAL POLYPS

The coral organism is a small anthrozoan polyp measuring about 1 cm. in length. It lacks a pedal disc and the oral disc bears tentacles in cycle of six. The pharynx is devoid of siphonogloyphs. The mesenteries follow the hexamerous plan and are restricted to the upper part of the polyp. The muscles are poorly developed.

Structure of coral polyp

In structure the coral polyp is much like an Anemone except the skeletal portions. The structure of the soft part is like sea anemone but

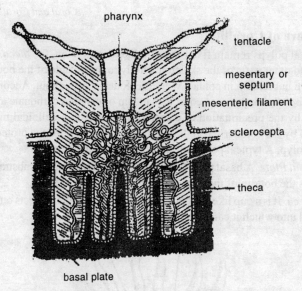

Fig. 8.4. V.S. through a coral in its theca (3 sclerosepta are shown).

pedal disc is absent. Basal region or pedal disc is occupied by skeletal cup. There is no oral cone. Mouth is situated in the middle of the oral disc. A typical oral disc with tentacles are simple and of moderate length ending in a terminal knob of nematocysts. A circular mouth surrounded by a flat peristomium leads into short stomodaeum or pharynx devoid of siphonoglyph. There are complete and incomplete septa or *mesenteries* arranged in cycles arranged on the typical hexamerous plan. Coral polyp being small does not possess more than three cycles of mesenteries. Usually two pairs of directives are present and there are ostia on the septa. The polyps of colonial corals are all interconnected but the attachment is lateral rather than aboral, as in hydroids. The column wall folds outward above the skeletal cup and connects with similar folds of adjacent polyps. Thus, all the members of the colony are connected by a horizontal sheet of tissue which represents folds of body-wall and so it contains an extension of the gastrovascular cavity as well as an upper and lower layer of endoderm and ectoderm. The lower ectodermal layer secretes the part of the skeleton that is located between the cups in which the polyps lie. The living coral colony thus lies entirely above the skeleton and completely covers it.

STRUCTURE OF CORAL SKELETON

The skeleton of a colony is termed as *corallum* and that of coral polyp a *corallite*.

Structure of Corallite

Coral polyps remain fixed in a cup like exoskeleton, the *theca*. The theca and other parts of the skeleton wholly to the outside of the body of the polyp but remain in contact with its ectoderm throughout. According to *Voucoch* the skeleton of coral is made up of calcium carbonate and is formed by the precipitation of calcareous crystals in a colloidal matrix secreted by the ectodermal cells outside the body wall for the protection of the polyp. A typical polyp coral has the following parts :

1. *Basal Plate.* A basal plate lies between the polyp and the substratum. It is the bottom of the cup.

2. *Theca.* It is a cup like structure from which the polyp projects outside and into which it can be retracted.

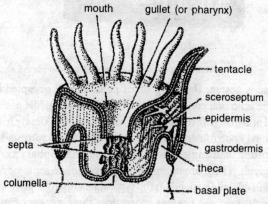

Fig. 8.5. One half of a simple coral polyp showing relationship of soft parts of theca (corallite)

3. *Sclerosepta.* These are calcareous ridges or partitions arranged vertically or projecting radially inwards and are connected at the base by basal plate and at the side with the cup like theca. They look like mesenteries but in fact lie between the mesenteries and thus lie in definite relation to them. Like the mesenteries, the sclero-septa typically, occur in hexamerous cycle, 12 tertiaries, 24 quaternaries etc; but other numbers are also met with. The sclerosepta are usually endocoelic i.e. each skeletal ridge pushes up between the two septa of a pair. The original second cycle is usually, however, exocoelic. The formation of the sclerosepta usually preceedes that of the corresponding septa (mesenteries) and thus there are often more sclerosepta than mesentry pairs. The first cycle of sclerosepta reach the columella, while the later one fall short of it and may fuse with

adjacent larger sclerosepta. It may be emphasized that the corallite lies entirely outside the body of the polyp and the polyp base is pushed into ridges over the sclerosepta and goes down into blind pockets between sclerosepta and mesentry.

The sclerosepta are commonly spiny, or thorny with toothed upper edges.

4. *Columella.* It is a pillar like irregular central skeletal mass which may be either an independent outgrowth from the basal plate or one formed by the union of the central ends of the sclerosepta, then called *pseudocolumella.* The columella may be solid or trabeculae.

5. *Epitheca.* It is distinct calcareous layer which surrounds the base of the theca in a ring-like manner.

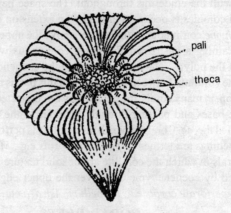

Fig. 8.6. Theca of a solitary coral showing pali.

6. *Costae.* The space between the theca and epitheca is crossed by continuation of the sclerosepta called costae.

7. *Pali.* Small ridges between the columella and the main parts of the sclerosepta are termed as pali.

8. *Synapticula.* These are the skeletal bars connecting adjacent sclerosepta.

9. *Dissepiments.* Horizontal plates between sclerosepta are known as dissepiments. These are of small extent.

10. *Trabeculae.* When the horizontal plates between sclerosepta are large and extend completely the corallite they are termed as trabeculae.

Formation of coral

The coral polyp develops from a planula which settles down and begins to secrete a skeletal rudiment or *prototheca*. It is secreted by ectoderm first as a basal plate. Following it, the larva develops radial folds which secrete septa (*sclerosepta*) and at the same time a rim is built up as a thecal wall around the polyp, laying at the top. Meanwhile, further skeletal material is added into the gaps between the septa. The septa of the skeleton usually alternate with the mesenteries of a living coelenterate.

In living condition, the polyp fills the whole of the interior of the corallite and projects beyond its edge. The proximal portion of its body wall is in contact with the theca which is a product of the epidermis. The free part of the body-wall of polyp is folded over the edge of the theca so as to cover its distal portion. Each skeletal septum is covered by an inturned portion of the body-wall. Thus the septa are actually external and are in contact with the epidermis throughout. The space between the theca of the coral colonies is occupied in life by an extension of the polyp walls, *coenenchyme* continuous with the later above the upper edge of the theca and containing a gastrovascular space continuous with gastrovascular cavity of the polyps. The lower surface of the coenenchyme secretes the part of the corallum between the theca, and this part is called *coenosteum*. In addition, in many corals, the polyps may be connected by canals coming from the bases and passing through openings in the loosely connected constructed thecae. Corals in which the corallite is perforated like this with many openings are termed as *perforate corals* e.g., *Madrepora* whereas those corals in which the corallite are of solid texture and the polyps are connected by coenenchyme only over the upper edge of the theca are called *imperforate corals* e.g. *Flabellum, Astraea* etc.

CORAL REEFS

A coral-reef is a ridge or mound of lime stone the upper surface of which is near the surface of the sea and which is formed of calcium carbonate by the action of organisms chiefly corals (*Vaughan,* 1917). Though the reefs are built by stony corals but other organisms such as Foraminifera, Millipora, Tubipores, Heliopores, the Molluscs, Echinoderms, some Coralline, Algae and Sponges constetute together in the formation of compact structure, the *coral reefs*. The coral reefs are formed by incrushing their skeletal parts on the deposited lime. Coral reefs composed of multiple of organisms vary in shape and colour. The zooxanthellae is responsible for the rich colouration of corals, which may be brown, yellow, or green. The reef building corals require warm, shallow waters, and consequently are limited to continental island shores in tropical and sub-tropical zones. They cannot tolerate temperatures below $18^0 C$ and they flourish nicely only above $22^0 C$. Consequently their distribution is limited to the zone existing between about 28° C on either side of the equator. They rarely remain alive at a depth greater than 4 fathoms.

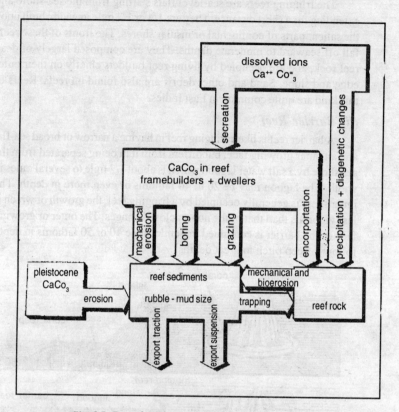

Fig. 8.7. Fate of calcium carbonate on a coral reef.

However, none of the reef types are like man made continous wall but is broken up into many reefs and islands by passages, the larger of which may be drowned valley, sunk below the sea by land subsequence or rise in sea level. The lagoons usually contain inner island, or island, and reefs, etc. The flats are more or less exposed at the lowest tides. The reef in front is exposed to forceful waves which knock off big and small fragments of the reef and leaves them up on the flat behind the reef edge. The reef front from first of all slopes gradually but after about 200 feet the slope becomes very steep.

Types of coral reefs

Coral reefs are of three types,

(i) Fringing reef, (ii) Barrier reef and (iii) Atoll

(i) Fringing Reef

The fringing reefs are sea-level flats starting from the sea-shore and extending for a short distance. They are 1/4 or 1/2 mile in width, built upon the salient parts of continental or insular shores. The fronts of these reefs fall off seaward to moderate depths. They are composed largely of dead reef rock, and are occupied by living reef builders chiefly on their outer edge and slope. Sand and other debris are also found on reefs. Reefs of this kind are quite common in East Indies.

(ii) Barrier Reef

A barrier reef is like a fringing reef in having a narrow or broad sea-flat and an outer growing face; but differs from it in being separated from the sea shore by a salt water lagoon which is about 1/2 mile to several miles in width. The lagoon may be 20 to 40 fathoms or even more in depth. The inner shore is generally occupied by a fringing reef, the growth of which is less vigorous than that of the non-enclosed fringes. The outer or growing face of the barrier is continued in gentle slope 40 or 50 fathoms in depth follow a steep pitch to great depths.

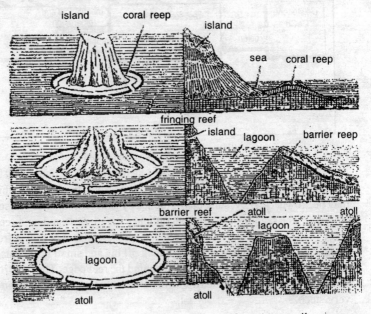

Fig. 8.8. Diagrams to represent different types of reefs, entire as well as in cross-section.

Barrier reefs are frequently interrupted by *passes* or *passages* through which even the ships may enter. Barrier reefs may encircle whole islands. Sometimes small islands may make their appearance in the protected lagoons. These reefs are sometimes a great danger to shipping. The Great Barrier reef of north-eastern Australia is about 1350 miles in length, about 20-70 miles wide and encloses a channel from 10 to 25 fathoms deep. At places it is about 90 miles away from the shore. Much of the reef is well below low tide. It is not a single reef but a long string of separate reefs whch are not always in a line. Inside the Great Barrier Reef are found various types of coral growths. There are hundreds of patches of oval or elongated coral islands built upto the surface. All have their own reefs.

(iii) Atoll

It is a coral island and consists of a belt of coral reef having a central shallow lake communicating with the sea. It is a horse shore-shaped or circular reef enclosing a *lagoon*. These lagoons are 40 or 50 miles across. Several of such atolls occur in the South Pacific. The *Atoll of Biknii* is very famous, which has a land of 287 square miles. Another atoll which is very famous due to prominence in World War II, is *Atoll of Tarawa*.

Growth of the coral to form reefs

Rate of coral growth is variable and of great importance. Slow growing massive types grow 5 mm. per year and fast-growing ones from 10 to 20 cm. per year. *Vaughan* estimated that a reef of 50 mm. deep is formed in 1,000 to 7,000 years and the age of the present reefs is 10,000 to 30,000 years.

Formation

The reefs are largely built by tiny polyps of the stony corals (order Madreporaria). The polyps secrete around them limestone cups, which coalesce to form large masses. The later, with the passage of time, take the form of huge rocks. Some other animals also take part in the formation of reefs. The hydrozoan *Millepora*, calcified alcyonarians *Tubipora* and *Helicopora*, and gorgonians add their skeletons to the reefs. The clams and tubeworms contribute their calcareous shell and tubes to the reefs. Lime secreting algae repair the windward edge of the reef by cementing loose pieces of coral rock into nearly solid reimparts. Sinking shells of foraminiferans fill the tiniest pores in the reefs. Whereas some organisms build up the reefs, others, like burrowing animals, break them down. This turns the reefs into labyrinths of ledges, crannies grottoes, crevices and tunnels.

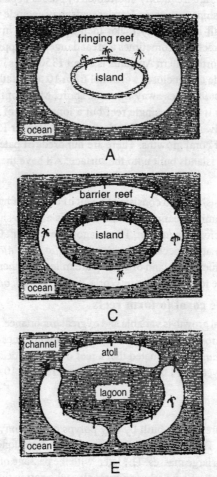

Fig. 8.9. Coral reefs. A—Fringing reef, B—Barrier reef, C—Atoll.

The coral reefs grow very slowly. Most of them expand at the rate of 10-200 mm. per year. The existing reefs seem to have been formed in 15,000 to 30,000 years.

THEORIES TO EXPLAIN GREAT VERTICAL
THICKNESS OF CORAL REEF

Since the present reef building corals do not grow below 150 feet at the outside, and becuase geological evidence indicates that corals of the past ages were also littoral, in their habits, it becomes essential to explain the great vertical thickness often attained by the coral reefs. Many theories have been propounded, which the following four are the main ones :

1. Darwin's Subsidence Theory

Charles Darwin's theory explains the formation of reef. According to him the reefs begin as fringe around slowly sinking shores, which continue to grow upward and outward as the land sinks. Thus the fringing reef turns into a barrier reef when coast subsides. The lagoon separating it from the reef becomes wider and wider. Islands surrounded by barrier reefs finally sink beneath the lagoon. Thus the encircling reef is left on which islands of wave tossed. Atolls are formed as accumulation of loose fragments of rocks.

2. Semper-Murray Solution Theory

Sir John Murray was the chief biologist on the 'Challenger', the British ship that sailed into the oceans from 1874 to 1876 to explore extensively the conditions and life in the sea. *Murrary* proposed that (i) Corals grow on high summits of the ocean bottom when these have been built up to the right level, (ii) the high summits are built by deposition of sediments and (iii) barrier reefs edge and through solution of the inner coral rock. This theory is now not accepted at all.

3. Submerged Bank Theory

This theory has been supported by many recent studies. According to this theory the coral formation grow on flat, pre-existing surface during or after the submergence of surfaces.

4. Daly Glacial-Control Theory

The main points of this theory are as follows : (i) During the last glacial period much water of the ocean turned into ice forming glaciers due to a very low temperature and thus the level of the ocean was lowered by 60 to 70 metres below the present level. (ii) Various terraces were then cut or islands levelled by wave action. (iii) Later, with the rising temperatures, corals began to grow upon these platforms and kept pace with the rising sea-level as the ice melted.

This theory explains nicely about the uniform depth of coral lagoons, whose bottoms, below the debris since deposited, would consist of the platforms cut when the ocean was at its low level.

Theories 3 and 4 supplement each other and at present are most favoured by the students of the problems, although Darwin's idea (Darwin-Dana subsidence theory) continues to find much support. The submergence theory agrees with Darwin's subsidence theory in that both consider the reef foundations to be now at great depths than they were when the coral growth started. But the submergence theory does not admit any relationship between that various kinds of reefs and postulates that the barrier reef and atoll have grown upon pre-existing flat platforms. The atolls are considered to have been shaped by winds, waves and currents.

Boring have been made to find out the truth of these theories.

(i) Boring of Funafuti atoll in the South Pacific north of Fiji was made in 1904 by an expedition of the Royal Society of London. The boring was 3 inches to 5 inches in diameter and went up to 1!14 feet without reaching the reef base. Twenty eight genera of reef building corals were discovered, 2 of which are now living on the reef in that locality above 60 metres. The material obtained from the boring did not contain any of the deep water corals lives in that locality at the depth to which the boring went. This finding supports subsidence theory.

(ii) *Cary* (1931) made 3 boring at different distances from the shore into a reef in Samoa (Pacific island) and concluded that the reef rested on a level platform cut by the action of waves. This supports the glacial control theory.

(iii) The Great Barrier Reef Committee made two boring, one in 1928 and the other in 1938 on the Great Barrier Reef. Both boring gave the same result that the coral material extended out only to 400 to 450 feet and below this there was nothing but sand containing shells of various animals. There was no evidence of any underlying platform. Therefore this finding also supports Darwin's subsidence theory. Thus Darwin's subsidence theory applies of many reefs but some reefs may have been laid down on pre-existing platforms.

Some important facts about reefs

Tropical storms can modify the reefs very much. Quarrying can also damage reefs as in India, where in 1971 *Pillai* has estimated that nearly 250 cubic meters of reefs material are removed per day for use in the production of cement, calcium carbide, calcium carbonate etc. Recently much concern has been expressed for the safety of some oceanic islands and their reef food chains because some reefs are being destroyed by ever increasing population of the Crown-of-thorns starfish, *Acanthaster planei*. These starfishes feed upon the living coral and have caused much reef destruction in some parts.

ECONOMIC IMPORTANCE OF CORAL REEFS

The coral reefs are of much importance to oil industry. They form highly favourable sites for the accumulation of petroleum deposits.

The coral reefs are of importance for *curio trade*. Many plant and animals like sponges, molluscs, fishes, echinoderms etc. grow on these reefs. Even some humans inhabit them.

Some corals form highly priced decorative pieces. *Corellium rubrem* is considered a precious stone. The red coral and organ pipe coral are used in medicine in South India. Skeleton of a few corals are used as building material.

Coral skeletons are also used in the formation of lime, mortar and cement. The skeletons are also used in making ridges which act as natural barriers against sea erosion and cyclonic storms.

The coral reefs serve as good nursery grounds for commercially important fishes. They form more colourful and beautiful fishes.

9

Polymorphism

Amongst the coelenterates, hydrozoans provide very good examples of polymorphism. The phenomenon is essentially for division of labour.Division of labour is first seen in the cells of *Hydra* where the cells are specialized to perform different functions of individual as a whole. Physiological differentiation of this type had its effect upon the morphology of cells which led to cells specialization and give rise to cells of differentt structures. In *Obelia* this specialization is carried still further. In it not only cells are specialized but individuals get specialized to perform different functions. The polyp perform different functions. The polyp performs vegetative function such as feeding, respiration, etc. and the free swimming medusae are reproductive in nature.

There are different types of polypoids and medusoids specialized for different functions. There are three types of polypoid and four types of medusoids individuals as given below :

I. POLYPOID ZOOIDS

1. Gastrozooids

The gastrozooids or the siphons are the nutritive or food-ingesting individuals of the colony. Each gastrozooid is a tubular or seccular structure with a large mouth. A single, long, contractile and hollow tentacle arises from the base of the gastrozooid. It bears numerous lateral contractile branches called the *tentilla,* each ending into a knob or coil of nematocytes.

2. Dactylozooids

These are the protective polyps of the colony and are variously known as *palpons, tasters* or *feelers.* Typically they resemble the gastrozooids except that they lack a mouth and their basal tentacle is unbranched. In *Vallela* and *Porpita* the dactylozooids arise from the margin of the colony in the form of long, hollow and tentacle-like fringing bodies called *tentaculozooids.* When associated with gonophores, the tentacle-like dactylozooids are known as *gonopalpons*. In *Physalia* the dactylozooids become excessively long

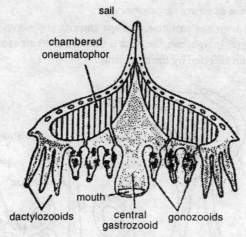

Fig. 9.1. Polypoid Zooids

3. Gonozooids

They are reproductive zooids which are also known as *blastostyles*. They are without mouth and tentacle. They reproduce asexually by budding and form medusae. In *Vallela* and *Porpita*, they resemble a gastrozooid and possess a mouth. Usually, the gonozooids take the form of branched stalks, called the *gonodendra*. These bear grape-like clusters of gonophores and are often provided with gonopalpons as in *Physalia*.

II. MEDUSOID ZOOIDS

1. Swimming bell

The *swimming bells* which are also known as *nectocalyces*, *nectophores* or *nectozooids* are medusoid form with a bell, velum, four radial canals and a ring canal. But these are devoid of mouth, manubrium, tentacles and sense organs. Its shape is variable and may be bilaterally symmetrical, prismatic, elongated or flattened. Due to well developed musculature, swimming bells act as excellent swimming organs and help in the locomotion of the colony.

2. Pneumatophores

The pneumatophores or the *floats* are bladder or vesicle-like structures filled with gas, and keep the colony floating. Each pneumatophore represents an inverted medusa bell, devoid of mesogloea and consisting of an external exumbrellar wall, *pneumatocodon*, and an internal subumbrellar wall, the *pneumatosaccus* or *air-sac*. The walls of both these are double-layered and are highly muscular. The space between the two walls is known as *gastrovascular cavity*.

A great degree of variation in shape and size is observed in different siphonophores. In *Agalima*, the float is simple and its air sac is lined by a layer of chitin secreted by the epidermis.

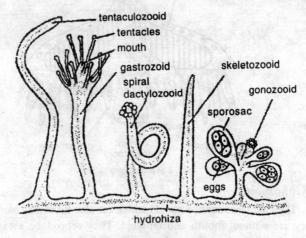

Fig. 9.2. Medusoid Zooids

The shape of pnematophone is variable and may or may not be divided into a number of concentric chitinous chambers arranged in one plane. These communicate with each other and with the central chambers by pores in their walls. The air sac may open or closed. The air sac may be perforated by a single or several pores. In some cases a portion of the float is partly constricted off and assumes the form of an ovoid medusa-like, called *aurophore*.

3. Bracts

The bracts which are also known as the *phyllozooids or hydrophyllia* are thick, gelatinous and curved plates of mesogloea. These may be prism-like, leaf-like, shield-like or helmet like in appearance. They are unlike meduase and contain a simple or branched gastrovascular canal.

4. Gonophores

The gonophores or the reporductive medusoids occur singly on separate stalks or in clusters on polypoid gonozooids as in *Velella* or on simple or branched gonodendra. The gonophores may be medusa-like with bell, velum, radial canals and a manubrium bearing gonads. But the mouth, tentacles and sense organs are always absent. In number of hydrozoans e.g. *Physalia,* the female gonophores are medusa-like while the male ones are sac-like. In animals, like *Physalia* (male), the gonophores may remain attached to the colony or are set free as in female *Physalia, Porpita* and *Velella.* Since they cannot feed, they perish after the discharge of sex-cells. The gonophores are dioecious but the colonies are hermaphrodite bearing both types of gonophores in the same or separate clusters. Gonophores may be budded off from the pedicel of the gastrozooid as in *Diphys,* or from a blastostyle as in *Velella* or from coenosarc as in *Agalmopsis.*

GRADES OF POLYMORPHISM

Some coelenterates possess only two types of zooids, others have three types and still others several types. These forms are respectively described as dimorphic, trimorphic and polymorphic. There are, thus three grades of polymorphisms :

1. Dimorphic Forms

The dimorphic forms have two types of individuals, namely, *polyps* or *hydranths* and *medusae.* These types are regarded as the fundamental types from which the additional types found in the trimorphic and polymorphic colonies are derived by modification.

(i) Polyps

The polyps have a cylindrical form, are fixed by aboral end, enclose a wide gastrovascular cavity, and bear mouth and tentacles at the free oral end. They serve to feed the colony and are, therefore, also known as the *gastrozooids* or *trophozooids.*

(ii) Medusae

The medusae have a bell -, bowl - or saucer-shaped body, lead free-swimming life when mature, enclose gastrovascular cavity in the form of narrow radial and circular canals, and bear mouth and marginal tentacles. They bear gonads and bring about sexual reproduction. They are, therefore, also known as the *gonozooids* or *sexual zooids.*

Though diverse in form and function, the polyps and medusae have a similar basic plan so much so that they can be derived from each other.

Bougainvillea. (Class Hydrozoa) and *Corallium* (class Actinozoa) are examples of dimorphic colonies.

(a) *Bougainvillea.* The polyps are stalked and uncovered, have an elongated manubrium and bear a sinlge circled of solid filiform tentacles. Medusae have four per-radial tufts of simple marginal tentacles and four groups of branched oral tentacles. They arise by budding from the hydrocaulus, polyp stalk and other medusae.

(b) *Corallium.* The zooids of *Corallium* are called *autozooids* and *siphonozooids.* Both are polypoid. The autozooids have tentacles and four groups of branched oral tentalces well developed mesenteries and a normal siphonoglyphe. They serve to feed coloney. The siphonozooids are small, lack tentacles, have reduced mesenteries and very large siphonoglyphe. They serve to drive a current of water through the cavities of the colony and bear gonad.

2. Trimorphic Forms

The trimorphic forms have three types of zooids, i.e., *polyps, medusae* and *gonozooids* or *dactylozooids.* The polyps and medusae are similar to those of dimorphic forms. The gonozooids are modified polyps. They lack mouth and tentacles. They serve to bud off medusae or their morphological equivalents. The dactylozooids are also modified polyps. They are mouthless and serve to protect the colony.

Example of trimorphic colonies are many. *Obelia* and *Millepora* are well known :

(a) Obelia

The zooids of *Obelia* include polyps, gonozooids and medusae. The polyps are surrounded by hydrothecae and gonozooids by gonothecae. The medusae are saucer-like and bear gonads on radial canals.

(b) Millepora

The zooids of *Millepora* include gastrozooids, dactylozooids and medusae. The gastrozooids have short plump body with mouth and four knob-like tentalces. The dactylozooids have a long, slender body without mouth but with several, short, alternating, knobbed tentalces. The medusae develop in pits or ampullae of the colony and are greatly reduced, being without velum, mouth, tentacles and canals. They bear four nematocyst-bearing knobs on the margin and gonads on the long manubrium.

3. Polymorphic Forms

The polymorphic forms have several types of zooids. All these are modifications of the polyps and medusae. The best known polymorphic forms are *Hydractinia* and members of the order Siphonophora.

(a) Hydractinia

Hydractinia develops four types of zooids : *gastrozooids, dactylozooids, gonozooids* and *sporosacs.* The dactylozooid have mouth and tentacles and feed the colony. The dactylozooid lack mouth and are defensive in function. They are further of two types : *spiral zooids* with short capitate tentacles and *tentaculozooid* which are long, slender and devoid of tentacles. The gonozooids retain short tentacles called the *nematocyst heads*. The sporosacs are reduced sac-like medusae. They produce gametes, either ova or sperms.

(b) Siphonophora

The siphonophores form free-swimming colonies with the highest degree of polymorphism. Their polyps occur in three modifications: gastrozooids, dactylozooids, and gonozooids.

(i) *Gastrozooids.* The gastrozooids are also called the siphonozooids, hence the name of the order. They feed the colony. They have the usual polyp form but lack the usually located tentacular ring. Instead, they bear a single, hollow, long and contractile tentalce at or near the base. The tentacle gives off lateral branches, the *tentilla,* each ending in a knob or coil of nematocysts.

(ii) *Dactylozooids.* The dactylozooids are also called the *palpons, feelers* or *tasters.* They lack mouth and their basal tentacle is unbranched. They may be long, hollow and tentacle-like, when they are termed the *tentaculozooids.*

(iii) *Gonozooids.* The gonozooids may look like the gastrozooids and even have a mouth, but lack a tentacle. Usually, however, they are long, slender and branched and are called *gonodendra.* They may bear tentacle-like dactylozooids called the *gonopalpons.* The gonozooids produce clusters of gonophores on them.

The medusoid individuals exist in four modifications : swimming bells, bracts, gonophores and pneumatophores.

(i) *Swimming Bells.* These are also termed the *nectophores* or *nectocalyces.* They are medusae with velum and radial and circular canals, but without mouth, manubrium, gonads and sense organs. They are very muscular and bring about locomotion of the colony.

(ii) *Bracts.* These are also called the *hydrophyllia* or *phyllozooids.* They are thick, gelatinous individuals with simple or branched gastrovascular cavity. They are protective in function.

(iii) *Gonophores.* The gonophores may be medusa-like but lack mouth, tentacles and sense organs. They may be reduced to rounded sacs. In some cases, the female gonophores are medusa-like and male gonophores are sac like. The gonophores produce gametes.

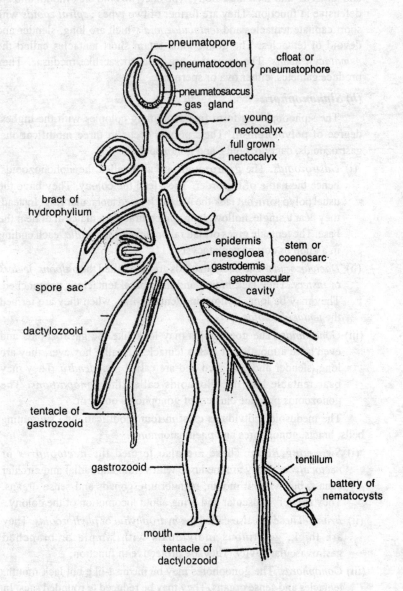

Fig. 9. 3. Diagrammatic V.S. of a siphonopore.

(iv) *Pneumatophore.* It is also known as the *float.* It is an inverted medusa
without mesogloea. Its outer (exumbrellar) and inner (subumbrellar)

wall are respectively called the *pneumatocodon* and *pneumatosaccus* or *air-sac*. The opening of the air-sac directed upwards, is reduced to a small pore, the *pneumatopore,* and is guarded by a sphincter muscle. At the bottom (original roof) of the air-sac, the epidermis is modified into a *gas gland* that secretes gas having composition similar to that of air. The float keeps the colony affloat.

All types of zooids arise by budding from a common *stem* or *coenosarc*. The latter may have the form of a tube or a disc and bears zooids in groups called *cormidia*.

The common polymorphic siphonophores are *Halistemma, Physalia, Vellela* and *Porpita*.

(a) Halistemma

Halistemma possess a long slender stem with a small float at the top, several close set swimming bells below the float and numerous cormidia lower down. The cormidia arise from nodes and each comprises a gastrozooid or dactylozooid and several sporosacs. Bracts arise from the internodes and partly cover the sporosacs.

(b) Physalia

Physalia has a disc-like coenosarc with a large sail-bearing, baloon-like float over it and several cormidia hanging from it. A cormidium consists or gastrozooids, small and large dactylozooids, gonodendra bearing gonophores, gonopalpons and peculiar gelatinous zooids of unknown function. The colony is poisonous.

(c) Velella

Velella has a rhomboidal float divided internally into a number of gas filled chambers. It bears an oblique sail above and a disk-like coenosarc beneath. There is a single, large, central gastrozooid surrounded by gonozooids which are, in turn, surrounded by dactylozooids. The gastrozooids lack a tentacle. The gonozooids have mouth and bear gonophores at the base. Dactylozooids are tentacles-like.

ORIGIN OF POLYMORPHISM

After studying the polymorphism in coelenterates, the question arises whether the metagenesis is a direct consequence of polymorphism or the life-cycle of primitive coelenterate has led to polymorphism. According to one view, the original coelenterate was a polyp and through specilization the sexual function was relegated to the secondarily developed medusoid form and this led to metagenesis. According to another view, the ancestral coelenterate was a medusoid form and the polypoid generation is persistent larval form, thus leading to polymorphism.

1. Polyp Origin Theory

This theory was proposed by *Huxley, Eschscholtz* and *Metshnikoff.* According to this theory component zooids, are really organs of a single medusoid inidividual, whose manubrium, tentacles and umbrella have become multiplied and migrated from their primitive positions. According to this theory, the various zooids are organs that have not yet attained the grade of polymorphic individuals, so that siphonophores are the most primitive existing coelenterates. In short, a siphonophore, in possessing a marked degree of power of vegetative increase of its parts, resembles a plant more than an animal. The theory errs too much in denying the colonial nature of siphonophores.

2. Polyp Person Theory

This theory was proposed by *Leuckart, Vogt* and *Gagenbaur.* According to this theory siphonophores are free-swimming polymorphic colonies of highly specialized polyps with the power to produce medusae. This theory maintains that the parts of a siphonophore are either polyps or medusae or both, but the primitive zooid of the colony is of the polyp type.

3. Sedgwick, Haeckel and Balfour

These three hold the view that the colonial theory (polyp-person theory) is more appropriate but that the primitive zooid of the colony was a medusa which has produced other medusa by budding and that the parts of these medusae possess the power of becoming discrete. Then they are removed from the bud to which they belong and in some cases, multiply secondarily. The many organsims of the colony, which according to the old colonial theory are modified polyps are, according to this view, nothing more than the parts of the medusiform inidivduals which have shifted their attachment and are therefore real organs. For instance the structures called palpons are to be looked upon as mouthless manubria of medusoid; the tentacles are to be looked upon as only surviving amongst the marginal tentacle of the medusoid. The theory agrees in asserting the colonial nature of Siphonophora but admits that there has been a vegetative repetition and specialization of certain organs which is demanded by the old colonial theory.

4. Moser's Theory

Recently, *Moser* has revived the polyp-organs theory of *Huxley* and *Metschnikoff.* According to *Moser,* the various individuals of siphonophore colony are organs that have not yet attained the grade of polymorphic individuals; and, therefore, the siphonophores are the most primitive existing coelenterates. Although the theory has not gained general recognition, yet it cannot be doubted that the siphonophores early diverged from the coelenterate stem.

We may, therefore, conclude that the identification of the component structures (especially in the siphonophores) as organs or individuals is a problem which rather defies an easy solution and may best be left as such.

Polymorphism and Alternation of Generations

Polymorphism is intimately associated with the life-history of organisms. In monomorphic forms as in *Hydra,* the life-cycle is simple and without any larval stage. It may be represented by the formula *polyp-egg-polyp.* With the advent of polymorphism, the reporductive power of the organisms is divided among the different individuals of the colony. In these organisms the polyps reproduce asexually to form medusoid form, the *gonophore,* and the gonophore reproduces sexually to form the *polyp.* The life-cycle of such organisms may be represented by the formula : *medusa-egg-planula-polyp.* Thus the *alternation of generations* or *metagenesis* comes into existence in the life-cycle-the asexual polypoid generation alternates with the sexual medusoid generation.

10

Skeleton in Coelenterata

The fossil record of the coelenterates skeleton is rich and dates back to the Ordovician period, about 350 million years ago. From the precambrian rocks of Ediacara Hills of S. Australia fossils have been found which belong to more then 600 million years ago.

Like sponges, the formation of skeleton is a common phenomenon in coelenterates. Their skeleton displays a good deal of variation. It serves

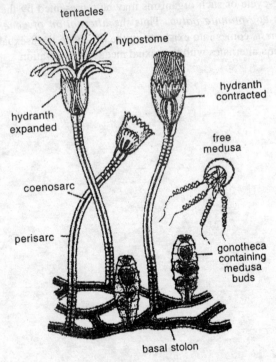

Fig. 10.1. *Campanularia.*

to support and protect the animal. It is ectodermal or mesodermal in origin. It may be *exoskeleton* or *endoskeleton*. The exoskeleton is secreted on the external surface while the endoskeleton in the mesenchyme. The skeleton may be in the form of separate pieces called *sclerites* or as a continuous mass. It Scyphozoa, the skeleton is altogether absent.

A. Skeleton in Hydrozoa

Among hydrozoans skeleton is found in Hydroida and Hydrocorallina. In Trachylina and Siphonophora, the skeleton is absent.

1. Order-Hydroida

Skeleton is absent in Hydras except the delicate cuticle over the epidermis. In Hydroida, the ectoderm secretes an outer chitinous transparent but tough cuticle called *perisarc* or *periderm*. It surrounds either the stem or branches or both of the individual hydranths or polyps.

The perisarc is firmer in the Caliptoblastea or Leptomedusae. In *Obelia, Sertularia, Plumularia* and *Campanularia,* the perisarc is continued upward to enclose the polyps and blastostyles. The perisarcal covering of polyp is called the *hydrotheca* and that of blastostyle is known

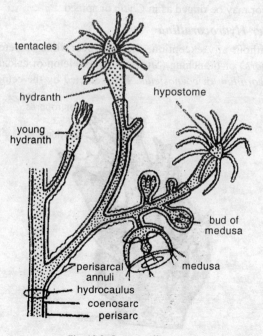

Fig. 10.2. *Bougainvillia*

as *gonothęca*. These zooids can withdrawn wholly or partially in the perisarcel coverings when disturbed. They are hence known as *thecata*.

In Gymnoblastea or Anthomedusae, the perisarc is confined to the hydrorhiza and the stalks of polyps. The polyps and blastostyles are without perisarcal covering i.e. they are naked. For this reason they are called *athecata*. The examples are *Bougainvillea, Tubularia, Pennaria* etc.

The perisarc forms rings or annulations below the zooids and near the origin of branches. The annulations are thought to impart a certain degree of flaxibility to the zooid.

The hydrotheca is often bell-shaped as in *Obelia* or tubular as in *Sertularia*. Its edges may be smooth or toothed (*Campanularia*). The hydrotheca may be open as in *Obelia* or covered by a lid or operculum as in *Diphasia* and *Sertulari*. The operculum may be made of one piece or many pieces. The operculum opens when the polyp is extended and closes when the polyp retracts. In many forms a circular or one-side chitinous shelf grows inward from hydrotheca to reduce the opening.

The gonotheca is often vase-like *Obelia*. It is generally smooth as in *Obelia* or may be ringed as in *Clytia* or spined.

2. *Order-Hydrocorallina*

Without any exception, the Hydrocorallina secretes a massive (*Millepora*) or branching (*Stylaster*) exoskeleton of calcium carbonate called *corallum* or *coenosteum*. It is secreted by the ectoderm. It thus

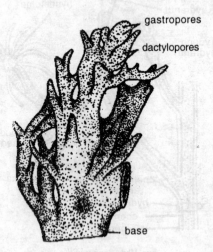

Fig. 10.3. *Millepora*.

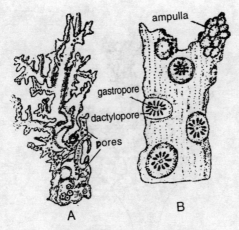

Fig. 10.4. *Stylaster.*

corresponds to the perisarc of hydroids. The surface of coenosteum is beset with numerous minute pores. The pores are of two sizes - the larger are *gastropores* and the smaller are *dactylopores*. The coenosarcal tubes bud off from their upper surface zooids. The zooids protrude out through these pores. The coenosteum forms upright, irregularly lobed or branched columns or encrusting mass as in *Millipora* and an elegant upright, tree-like growth abudantly branched in one plane in *Stylaster*. In *Stylaster* the branches bear circular elevations, each with cup-like cavity having deeply grooved walls. The cavity is occupied by gastrozooids and the groove by dactylozooid.

B. Skeleton in Anthozoa

A few anthozoan have permanently soft bodies while the majority of them are supports by skeleton.

1. Alcyonaria

The skeleton is internal in Alcyonaria. The skeleton is either calcarious or horny or partly calcarious and partly horny and in the form of *spicules*. The spicules are secreted by mesogleal cells, the *scleroblasts* of coenenchyme. The seleroblasts are amoeboid cells that migrate from the epidermis. Various modifications of the spicules provide an important taxonomic characters. The spicules are in the forms of slender, pointed, monoaxial, often with edges, tubercles, spines, plates etc. The simplest skeleton is seen in *Hartea* where minute irregular spines of $CaCO_3$ are deposited in mesenchyme. A simplar skeleton of calcareous spicules of varying forms occurs in *Alcyonium*. In Gorgonacea, the skeleton consists of branched axis. It is very hard and composed of calcareous spicules

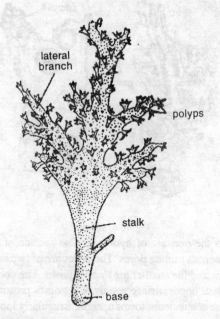

Fig. 10.5. *Alcyonium*.

cemented together by $CaCO_3$ in *Corallium* but flexible and made up of horny material (*gorgonin*) in *Gorgonia*. In some Gorgonacea, the axial skeleton is partly horny and partly calcareous. Besides axial rod, calcareous spicules of various shapes are found in the mesogloea of the coenosarc. In Blue coral, *Heliopora*, the skeleton is stony and massive. It is not formed by the fusion of spicules, but it is solid from the begining and is composed of crystalline fibres of aragonite fuses lamellae.

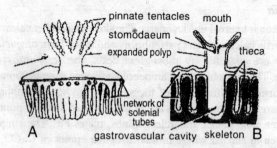

Fig. 10.6. *Heliopora*. A—A complete polyp. B—Polyp in vertical section.

In *Tubipora*, the originally separate calcareous warty spicules fuse to form a continuous tube in each polyp and a solid platform in each

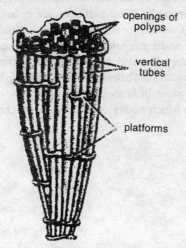

openings of polyps

vertical tubes

platforms

Fig. 10.7. *Tubibora.*

horizontal stolon. In *Pennatula,* the sea-pen, the skeleton consists of an unbranched axial rod of calcified horny axis situated in primary polyp and of scattered, variously shaped, smooth, calcareous spicules present in the mesogloea of entire colony. Some of the spicules are microscopic, others readily visible to neked eyes.

2. Zoantheria

In Zoantharians there is exoskeleton and it is ectodermal in origin. The skeleton may be calcareous and massive horny and arborescent, but never made up of spicules. The Actiniaria (sea-anemones) lack a true skeleton. However, some have a thick cuticle and a few, like *Edwardsia,* enclose themselves in a more or less complete tube formed of discharged nematocysts. Zoanthidea and Ceriantharia are without any skeletal formation. The column is usually covered by a thick cuticle and is often encrusted with foreign matter like sand grains, sponge spicules, forameniferan ooze etc. In Antipatharia (*Antipathes*) the skeleton consists of an axial rod formed of a flexible, horn-like material identical to gorgonin chemically. The axis is brown or black in colour and bears simple, branched or papillated thorns. The skeletal system of Madreporaria comprising the true or stony corals, is entirely different from that of other coelenterates. The skeleton is in the form of a massive calcareous epidermal exoskeleton. It is known as *corallite* in solitary individual and as *corallum* in the case of colony. A corallite has the form of a cup. The polyp that secretes it lies in it. The corallite enlarges as its polyp grows.

From the inner surface of the wall of corallite a number of vertical partitions extend inwards. There partitions are called *sclerosepta*. The sclerosepta are of several orders—primary, secondary and tertiary according to their width the sclerosepta are made up of fuse rod-like skeletal elements, the trapeculae. At the centre of the corallite is an upright pyramid, the *columella*. The flattened bottom of the cup beneath the polyps is called the *basal plate*. In *Flabellum*, the basal plate is produced into a short peduncle by which young coral remains attached becoming free when adult.

11

Economic Importance of Coelenterata

Coelenterates have very little economic importance. Certain jelly fishes are eaten in the oriental region, two anthrozoans are eaten in Italy. However, they form the food of many fishes, molluscs and crustaceans. Some coelenterates have relations with other animals. The corals build reefs which also produce islands that are put to various uses by human beings.

Certain corals are very beautiful, having attractive colours. These corals are used in the formation of jewellary. Certain coelenterates like *Millepora, Tubipora* etc. are used as decarative pieces in houses and in aquaria. Certain coelentrates form good material for research purposes. These are used in the experiment of development, regeneration etc.

RELATIONS WITH OTHER ORGANISMS

The coelenterates are predaceous, many forms carry on relationship with them as they could easily use as food. Various types of relationships with other animals can be studied under following headings :

1. Commensal relations

Commensalism is a phenomenon where one organism living in or on another, with only one of the two benefiting. Many hydroid live commensally on sponges, molluscs, gorgonians etc. and floating plant species. For example *Hydractinia* grows on the shell of *Buccium* (a gastropod mollusc). The shell is inhibited by a hermit crab. Species of sea-anemones are often carried about on the shells of snail inhibited by hermit crab. The hermit crab acquires immunity to the poison of sea-anemone by feeding on its tentacles.

Hermit crab (*Eupagurus prideauxi*) can recognize the particular species of sea-anemones (*Adamsia palliata*) by touching. The hermit crab carries the anemone about in an in separable partnership where the crab moves to a large shell due to growth, the anemone is also detached and placed on the new shell. The hermit crab is protected from its enemies by the stinging power of the anemone due to nematocysts and acontia and may share food caught by the anemone. In return, the anemone also benefits as it is carried about by the hermit crab getting better chances to obtained food and also shares food particles dropped by the crab. This is an example of *mutualism.*

Association between corals and a crab (*Hapalocarcinus*) and shrimps is remarkable. A young female crab comes to rest in a fork of the coral. Due to water currents created by the gills of crab, the growth pattern of coral is affected. In due course of time, the coral grows forming a chamber. In the chamber the female crab is inclosed. Here it can never escape but enjoys safety from its enemies. Small openings of chamber permit the entry of tiny males and also the minute planktons for the female crab.

Another interesting case of immunity occurs between a small fish *Nomeus* and *Physalia.* Formar lives in commensalism with later, swimming harmlessly among its omnious tentacles. When pursued by larger fishes, it often sinks refuge there and leads the pursuers to their doom. If separated from its protector, *Nomeus* will dash back quickly. Thus *Nomeus* is said to build up an immunity to the hypnotoxin of the *Physalia* by feeding on its tentacles.

Several species of *Trapezia* live particularly with living branched reef corals, but never inhibit the dead ones.

2. Symbiotic relations

Several species of unicellular algae called *Zooxanthellae* live as intracellular symbionts in the gastrodermal cells of different regions in a number of coelenterates. During day time the algae produce oxygen by photosynthesis, by utilizing carbon dioxide which is produced by the coelenterate cells respiration. During photosynthesis food and oxygen are produced which are utilized by the coelenterate.

According to *Goreau* (1961), the zooxanthellae plays an important role in the formation of skeleton is coral polyps. It removes carbonic acid (H_2CO_3) from calcium bicarbonate to form calcium carbonate.

$$Ca(HCO_3)_2 \rightleftharpoons CaCO_3 + H_2CO_3$$

The above process occurs only where illumination of light is there.

3. Parasitic relations

Certain snails of family Margilidae live parasitically embedded in the tissue of soft corals and gorgonians to suck juice from their hosts.

Hydrichthys, a parasitic colonial coelenterates lives upon fishes, attached by a network. It sucks the nourishment directly by penetrating hydrorhizal stolons into the host tissue.

4. Predator relationship

Nearly all the coelenterates are carnivorous feeding upon minute planktons. On the other hand, many coelenterates are consumed as food by other predator animals. Certain snails (*Janthina, Fiona* and *Glaucus*, prey upon the pelagic of *Velella* and *Porpita*).

RELATIONS TO MAN

1. Food

As food, the coelenterates are little used by man. However, some jelly fishes are eaten in the oriental region. Two species of sea-anemones are also eaten in Italy under the name of Ogliole.

2. Corals

The stony corals produce calcareous reefs and ultimately dry lands. Corals of geological part were favorable sites for accumulation of petroleum deposits. The hard coral lime can be used for building purposes.

3. Decorative materials

Some corals are very beautiful and have been used as ornaments or in decorative art from old times. The red coral (*Corallium rubrum*) commonly known as *red moonga* is used in jewellery. Others (*Tubipora, Gorgonia* etc.) are used in indoor aquariums etc. *Sertularia*, collected from English channel, is dried, dyed bright green and sold as 'air fern' for decorative purpose.

4. Biological experiments

Coelenterates are used in laboratories to demonstrate the phenomenon of budding, grafting, regeneration etc.

5. Harmful coelenterates

The coelenterates, possessing the nematocysts or stinging cells, directly affecting man. *Aurelia* can produce an uncomfortable burning sensation. *Physalia*, the Portuguese man-of-war, is one of the most dangerous free-swimming species. It has long trailing tentacles reaching upto 32 meters in length. It can inflict painful and often serious stings on helpless swimmers. Its poison is neurotoxic affecting the nervous system, to man it can cause agonising, burning pains and brings about collapse and unconsciousness.

12

Ctenophora : Characters & Classification

Phylum Ctenophora (Gr. *Ktenos*-of a comb; *phoreo*-to bear) includees a small group of free swimming marine animals that are even more transparent than the coelenterate jelly fishes. They have been placed by many authors under the phylum Coelenterata, but the present tendency is to separate tham from coelenterates and rank them as a distinct phylum (*Hatschek*, 1839). They are widely distributed, being especially abundant in warm seas.

Characters

1. These are free-swimming, marine and solitary animals. The polymorphism and attached stages are absent.
2. Body transparent, gelatinous, pear-shaped, cylindrical or flat ribbon-shaped.
3. Biradial symmetry along an oral-aboral axis.
4. A pair of long, solid, retractile tentactes are present.
5. Eight comb-like ciliary plates are present on the body for locomotion.
6. Cell-tissue grade of organisation.
7. Nematocysts are absent. *Colloblasts* or *lasso-cells* are special adhesive cells present on the tentacles for food capture.
8. Body acoelomate and triploblastic with an outer epidermis and inner endodermis or gastrodermis. The middle jelly-like mesogloea is present with scattered cells and muscle fibres.
9. Digestive system comprises a mouth, pharynx, stomach (forming a complex system of gastrovascular canals) and two aboral anal pores.
10. Skeletal, circulatory, respiratory and excretory systems are absent.
11. Nervous system is diffused type. The aboral end bears a sensory organ, the *statocyst*.
12. All are bisexual or monoecious. Endodermal gonads develop side by side on gastrovascular canals.

13. A sexual reproduction is absent.
14. Development is indirect, includes a characteristic *Cydippid larva.*
15. Alternation of generation is absent.
16. Regeneration and paedogenesis are of common occurrence.

CLASSIFICATION

There are about 100 species in Phylum Ctenophora. These are divided into two classes.

Class-1. Tentaculata

1. These are ctenophores in which two long aboral tentacles are present. In some only the larva bears tentacles.
2. Narrow mouth and small pharynx is present.

The class tentaculata is divided into 4- orders :

Order-1. Cydippida

1. Body is simple, rounded or oval.
2. No anal pores, as the digestive canal terminates blindly.
3. Two long and branched tentacles, retractile into sheath.

Examples : *Pleurobrachia, Mertensia, Homiphora.*

Order-2. Lobata

1. Body is laterally compressed and oval.
2. Two large oral lobes and four slender flap-like auricles around mouth.
3. In larva tentacles are pouched but pouches are absent in adult.
4. The gastrovasular canals are connected by a ring canal at the oral end.

Examples : *Bolinopsis, Mnemiopsis.*

Order-3. Cestida

1. Body elongated and compressed, ribbon-like.
2. 4 rows of rudimentary and 4 rows of prominant comb-plates are present.
3. Two main tentacles present in sheaths but reduced. Along oral edge many small tentacles are present.

Examples : *Cestum, Velamen.*

Order-4. Platyctenea

1. Body is much flat, oral-aborally compressed.
2. Two well developed tentacles with sheaths.
3. Comb-plates often absent in adults.
4. Adapted for creeping.

Examples : *Ctenoplana, Coeloplana.*

Class-2. Nuda

1. The tentacles and oral lobes are absent.
2. Body large, conical and laterally compressed.
3. Wide mouth and large phrynx.

Order-1. Beroida

1. Voracious feeders.
2. Conical, with a wide mouth and pharynx, and with meridional, ramified, gastrovascular canals.

   Example : *Beroe.*

CESTUM

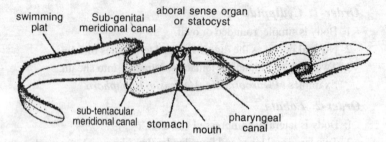

Fig 12.1. *Cestum.*

1. *Cestum* is commonly known as *Vinus's girdle.*
2. It inhibits warmer seas, especially the mediterranean.
3. Body is greatly elongated horizontally, in the plane of stomach, but compressed laterally so that it appears ribbon like.
3. It is about 8 cm wide and one meter long.
4. It is usually green, blue or violet coloured.
5. It swims by muscular undulations of the body, as well as by the beating of the comb-plates.
6. Eight comb-plates are present.
7. Out of these 8 plates, four are very small and other four are continued all along the aboral edge of the body.
8. Small comb-plates are confined to the vicinity of the sense organ (statocyst).
9. In adult, the principle tentacles are rudimentary and located in deep sheaths besides the mouth.

10. Numerous small simple and lateral tentacles spring from grooves, which are continued in the whole length of the oral edge.

CTENOPLANA

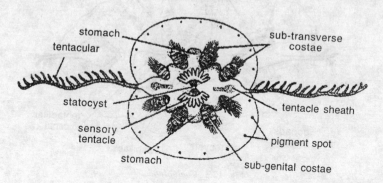

Fig. 12.2. *Ctenoplana* (Dorsal view).

1. *Ctenoplana* is a small marine, solitary, planktonic animal, living in the surface waters of sea.

2. The body is nearly circular in outline, flattened dorso-ventrally. It measures 6 mm. in diameter.

3. The dorsal surface is olive green, brown or reddish in colour.

4. In the centre of aboral surface, there is a sense organ with a statolith surrounded by a ring of small ciliated tentacles arranged bilaterally into two groups of 8 each.

5. Mouth is present on oral or ventral surface. Locomotory organs are small deeply sunk swimming plates.

6. The gastrovascular canal system is devoid of meridional canals but comprises a set of branching and anastiomosing peripheral canals.

7. Gonads occur as four bilobed masses in the walls of sub-tentacular canals. The muscular system is highly developed.

COELOPLANA

1. *Coeloplana* is a marine solitary animal found in the Red Sea on the coasts of Japan, Florida and West Indies.

2. The body is oval and dorsal-ventrally flattened but elongated in tentacular plane. Its length is about 60 mm.

3. The mouth is ventral in position.

4. Statocyst is dorsal.

5. Tentacles are paired and retractile.

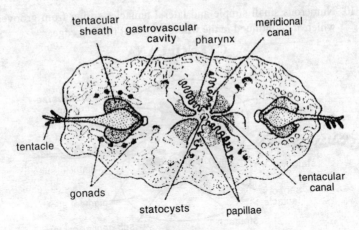

tentacular
sheath   gastrovascular   meridional
cavity   pharynx   canal

tentacle

gonads

statocysts   papillae

tentacular
canal

Fig. 12.3. *Coeloplana.*

6. It moves by creeping.

7. The swimming plates do not occur, although traces of the ciliated furrows exit.

8. Upper surface bears more or less symmetrical arranged tuberculate papillae containing extensions of gastrovascular canals.

9. Gonads are present in the walls of meridional gastrovascular canals.

10. Fertilized eggs become attached by a sticky secretion to the ventral surface of the mother.

11. Each egg develops into a typical cydippid larva with comb-plates.

12. After free swimming for some times the larva undergoes metamorphoses into *Coeloplana*.

BEROE

1. It is commonly known as *sea mites* or *mitre jelly-fish*.

2. It is found in great swarms and has cosmoplitan distribution.

3. Its body is conical measuring 10 to 20 cm. in length.

4. It is laterally compressed and pink in colour.

5. The rounded aboral end bears the sense organ surrounded by rounded polar fields edged with numerous branching papillae.

6. The oral end is truncated and is occupied by a wide mouth.

7. The swimming plates are of equal length extending from over half to nearly the entire length of body in different species.

8. The interior of the body is occupied by stomodaeum or pharynx.

9. The pharyngeal canals run close to the surface of body. Stomach is small lying near aboral pore.

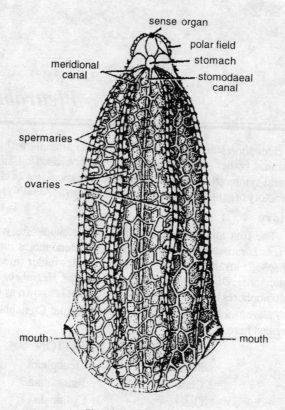

Fig. 12.3. *Beroe.*

10. It gives rise 4 inter-radial canals which bifurcate to form 8-meridionel canals.

11. The meridional canals give off numerous branched lateral diverticula which anastomose to form a complex network through the mesenchyme.

12. Tentacles are absent. It is voracious feeder, swallowing crustaceans and sometimes other ctenophores even larger than itself.

Revision Questions

1. Classify Ctenophora giving characters and examples of each group and discuss its affinities.

2. Discuss the affinities and systematic position of Ctenophora.

3. Write short notes on ? (a) *Cestum*, (b) *Beroe*, (c) *Ctenoplana.*

13

Pleurobrachia

The ctenophores are free-swimming marine animals with transparent gelatinous bodies showing biradial symmetry based on an underlying bilateral symmetry. They bear comb-like ciliary plates as characteristic locomotory organs. They are commonly known as "*comb-jellies*".

History

The first and definite description of ctenophores was given by *Martens.Linnaeus* and *Cuvier* placed some ctenophores into Zoophyta. *Eschscholtz* arranged the pelagic coelenterates under three orders viz, *Ctenophorae, Discophorae* and *Siphonophorae, Hatschek* (1889) put all the ctenophores under a distinct phylum, what is known as Ctenophora.

Pleurobrachia, a typical example of Phylum Ctenophora has been described here.

SYSTEMATIC POSITION

Phylum	-	Ctenophora
Class	-	Tentaculata
Order	-	Cydippida
Genus	-	*Pleunobrachia*

Habits and Habitat

It is a common marine animal often occuring in enormous groups. They are abundant in the warmer seas.They are of planktonic habit, floating in the surface water, however, few ctenophores live up to the depth of 3000 meters. The ctenophores are voracious carnivorous, feeding on planktons, eggs and larvae of molluscs, crustaceans and fishes.

EXTERNAL FEATURES

The general body shaped resembles more or less like a meduse of coelenterates.

Shape

Pleurobrachia is somewhat spherical, pear- shaped or cylindrical in shape that is why they are commonly known as *sea-walnuts*. The outer surface is without any hard skeleton. The body is divided into two hemispheres. The mouth lies at the oral end and a sense organ at the aboral end of the body.

Size

Pleurobrachia meaures about 2 cm. in diameter. Some ctenophores like *Cestum* meaures upto 75cm. in length.

Colour

Ctenophores are usually transparent, but some structures like tentacles and comb rows ae tinged with white, orange or purple colours.

Symmetry

The animal is biradial symmetrical, since the parts, though in general radially disposed, lie half on one side and half on other side of median longitudinal plane.

MORPHOLOGY

The mouth is situated at the oral end and the sense organ at the aboral end. Extending from near the oral surface to near the aboral end are eight meridional rows of comb. plates, grouped in pairs. A typical plate is 800 mm long and 30 mm by 600 mm at the base. Such plates occupy parallel planes and are spaced at an interval of 300-400mm within the rows. Each comb- plate bears about 10^5 cilia. The cilia are held together in rows more less firmly by lamellar connection. The whole comb-plate functions as a single unit. In spite of its large size, the pattern of beat is very similar to that of cilia of shorter magnitude. While effecting locomotion the comb-plates are rapidly lifted in the direction of the aboral pole and than lowers slowly to their normal position. Those in each row beat one another starting from the aboral to the oral end. All the eight rows beat in unison and the animal propelled through water with the oral end in front. The aboral end bears two long - branched tentacles. The tentacles are solid and retractile. They are not attached to the body surface but each emerges out from a *tentacular sheath*. The sheath is a deep ciliated epidermal blind pouch into which the tentacle can be wholly or partly withdrawn. Each tentacle bears a single row of short latral branches or pinnae. The tentacles are solid and the core is made up of mesenchyma covered with epidermis, containing muscle fibres. The nematocysts are absent.The tentacles are supplied with adhesive cell called *colloblasts* or *lasso*. The colloblasts produce a stick secretion of use in the capturing small animals, which serve as food. The spiral filament in each colloblast is contractile and acts as spring, often preventing the struggling prey from tearing the cell away. The tentacles do not help in locomotion.

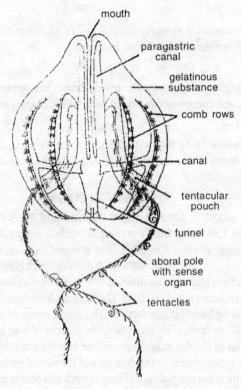

Fig. 13.1. *Pleurobrachia*.

Body Wall

The body wall is made up of outer *epidermis*, middle *mesogloea* and inner *gartodermis* or *endodermis*.

The ectodermal cells are columnar or cuboidal epithelial cells. These cells are interspread with numerous mucous gland cells and sometimes certain pigmented granules or branched pigment cells. The sensory cells are also present and are of two types- the first type having several stiff bristles and other type having single stout bristle.

The mesogloea is thick gelatinous layer having muscle, nerve fibres and amoeboid cells.

The endoderm lines the gartrovascular canals, and stomach. It is made up of tall, vacuolated and ciliated cells.

Digestive System

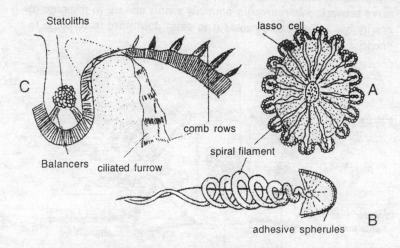

Fig. 13.2. A- Cross Section of a tentacles; B- Colloblast; and C- Part of anterior end of a Ctenophore showing statocyst. ciliated groove and Comb-plates.

The *mouth* lies in the centre of oral end. It is a slit-like aperture that leads into a long, tubular and sagittally flattened tube, the *pharynx* . The pharynx has folded walls containing long, ciliated epidermal and gland cells. The pharynx opens into a small but wide *stomach*. Six canals arise from stomach. Two of these, called *anal canals,* open to the exterior near the sense organ. The undigested food passes through them, or is ejected through the mouth. The two *paragastric canals* lie parallel to pharynx or stomodaeum, ending blindly near the mouth. The two tentacular canals pass out towards the pouches of tentacles, then each tentacular canal gives rise to four branches, these lead into *meridional canals* lying just beneath the comb-plates.

Nervous System and Sense Organ

The nervous system is a sub-epidermal nerve network of multipolar ganglion cells and neurites with synaptic connections. Nerve fibres extend to the muscles in mesogloea.

The aboral sense organ is a *statocyst*. It is the organ of equilibrium. It consists of a vesicle of fused cilia enclosing a ball of calcareous granules, the *statolith*. The statolith is supported by four tufts of fused cilia called *balancer cilia*. The balancer cilia respond to changed pressure from the statolith by modifying the beat of the comb-plates they had. The impulse from balancer cilia seems to be transmitted by a cell to cell conduction in the epidermis, although inhibitor stimuli are transmitted by an underlying nerve network. *Pleurobrachia* normally swims upward in response to gravity but a disturbance causes it to swim downward in response to gravity.

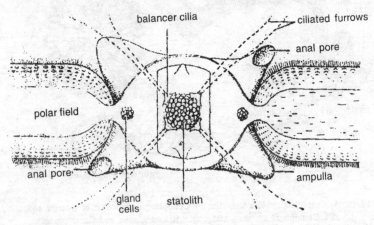

Fig. 13.3. Statocyst of a *Ctenophore*.

Respiration

The respiratory organs are absent. Each cell takes oxygen from the surrounding water by diffusion and eliminates carbon dioxide. Water circulating within the gastrovascular canal system brings oxygen to the tissues of interior and takes away carbon dioxide.

Excretion

Cell-rosettes are reported to present in the walls of the gastrovascular canals. Each rosette includes a circle of ciliates gastrodermal cells, guarding a minute opening between the lumen of gastrovasular canal and the mesogloea. Probably the nitrogenous waste or excess fluid passes through their openings from mesogloea into the gastrovascular canals.

Reproductive System

The ctenophores are hermaphrodite, reproduce sexually by the production of sperms and ova. The gonads are developed in the form of bonds in the meridional canals. The ova are formed on one side and the sperms on the other side of each maridional canal just beneath the comb - plates. The mature ova and sperms are discharged into the canals where fertilization takes place and finally the zygotes escape through the mouth.

Development

After fertilization, the egg undergoes holoblastic and determinate cleavage. The first two divisions are meridional which give rise to four blastomeres. The third cleavage is vertical resulting in a curved plane of eight cells arranged into two rows. Next divisions are horizontal give rise to eight micromeres and eight megameres. The micromeres give rise to the ectoderm while megameres give rise to endoderm. A solid *blastula* results. By epiboly and invagination the blastula gives rise to a *gastrula*. A free swimming *cydippid* larva is formed. The larva is similar in general structure to adults. The larva directly forms the adult or through a gradual metamorphosis.

Some ctenophores exhibit a peculiar phenomenon called *dissogeny*, in which both, larva and adult resproduce sexually. In warm weather cydippid larva becoms sexually mature.

AFFINITIES OF CTENOPHORA

The ctenophores possess many characters of coelenterates. For long some writers regarded as a class of phylum Coelenterata and placed them under Sub-phylum *Acnideria* together with Sub-phylum-*Cnideria*. The affinites of Ctenophora are as follow:

1. Resemblance with Coelenterata

1. Presence of biradial symmetry and tentacles.
2. Arrangement of parts along an oral - aboral axis.
3. Coelom is absent.
4. Body wall is two cell layered with a gelatinous mesogloea in between.
5. Presence of branched endodermal gastrovascular cavity.
6. A mouth leads from the gastrovascular cavity to outside.
7. Organ systems are absent.
8. Presence of diffused nerve net.
9. Presence of statocyst.
10. Gonads are endodermal in origin.
11. Presence of colloblasts similar to the nematoblarts of the coelenterates. Presence of nematoblasts in *Euchlora rubra (ctenophore)* is an evidence of the coelenterate origin of ctenophore.

Due to above similarities the ctenophores are considered by many zoologists to be a class of phylum coelenterate.

2. Resemblance with Hydrozoa

An anthomedusan form, *Ctenaria,* presents remarkable similarities with cyclippid in the following characters:

1. Presence of two tentacles, which are situated at the opposite per-redii in sheath.
2. The general body surface of a ctenophore corresponds with the exumbrella surfaces of medusa.
3. Both possess a thick, gelatinous mesogloea.
4. Presence of eight radial canals formed by the bifurcation of four inter-radial pouches of stomach, correspond with them are eight bands of nematocysts diverging from the apex of exumbrella.

But these similarities are superficial following dissimilarities clearly show that *Ctenaria* is not an intermediate between coelenterates and ctenophores.

1. The tentacles of *Ctenaria* have no muscular bases.
2. Eight rows of nematocysts of *Ctenaria* are not homologous to rows of comb-plates of a ctenophores.
3. *Ctenaria* is radially symmetrical while ctenophores are biradial symmetrical.
4. The gonds are endodermal in origin in ctenophores but in *Ctenaria* is ectodermal in origin..
5. In *Ctenaria* aboral sense organ is absent.

Hydroctena, a narcomedusan, also presents some striking though superficial ctenophoran resemblance in possessing an aboral sense organ and a pair of tentacles in sheaths.

3. Resemblance with Anthozoa

1. Ciliated ectoderm of anthozoan is probably a forerunner of the ciliated band of ctenophore.
2. Well developed stomodeum is present.
3. The gut in embyos of both is four-lobed, thus representing biradial symmetry.
4. The gonads develop from endoderm and the gametes or zygote passed out through the mouth.

But the aboral sense organ and rows of comb-plates of a ctenophore have no parallel parts in an anthozoan. Moreover, the colloblasts differ structurally from the nematocysts. The tentacles are solid in ctenophores but hollow in anthozoans.

Differences from Coelenterates

Ctenophores differ from coelenterates in the following respects.

1. The tentacles are oppositely placed suggesting a biradial symmetry.
2. Aboral sensory organ it present in the form of statocyst.
3. Namatocysts are absent except in one or two cases.
4. Presence of eight locomotory meridional ciliated bands of comb-plates over the body.
5. Tentacles bear colloblasts.
6. Mesenchymal muscles are present.
7. Definite organisation of digestive system with anal pores.
8. The development is deteminate type.

Affinities with platyhelminthes

The ctenophore, (*Coeloplana* and *Ctenoplana*) exhibits many structural similarities with turbellarian platyhelminth . There are:

1. Epidermis is ciliated.
2. Body is dorso-ventrally flattened. Crawling mode of life.
3. Origin of mesoderm is more or less similar.
4. The dorsal polar nerve of turbellarian can be compared with statocysts of ctenophores.
5. During development similar segmentation and gastrulation.

The view that primitive Bilateria have evolved through Platyctenea (*Ctenoplana* and *Coeloplana*) has not been accepted. The Platycetenea are considered typical ctenophores adapted for creeping mode of life. Platyctenea is a tissue-grade diploblastic animal whereas turbellarian is an organ-grade triploblastic form.

Conclusion

Ctenophore exhibit many striking characteristics of their own such as prominent apical organ; mode of origin of musculature from mesogloea; presence of gonoducts and determinate type of cleavage. Thus, it seems more logical to treat them as a separate phylum, rather than a class of phylum of Coelenterata.

Revision Questions

1. Describe various life process of *Pleurobrachia*.
2. Discuses the affinities of Ctenophora.

Index